TANKS AND ARMORED
FIGHTING VEHICLES OF WWII
THE WORLD'S GREATEST MILITARY VEHICLES, 1939–1945

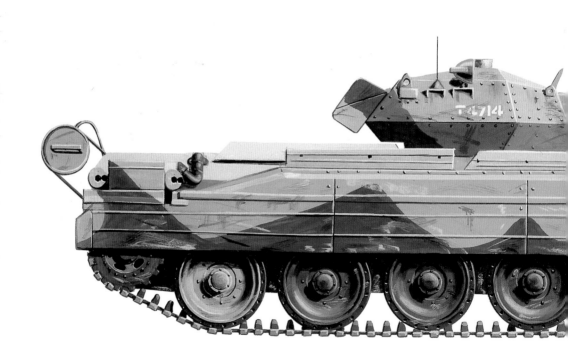

TANKS AND ARMORED
FIGHTING VEHICLES OF WWII

THE WORLD'S GREATEST MILITARY VEHICLES, 1939–1945

Jim Winchester

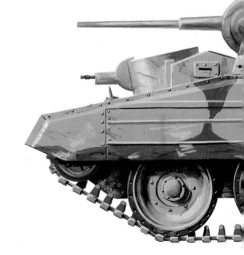

**BARNES
&NOBLE
BOOKS**

NEW YORK

This Barnes & Noble edition 2004

Published by
Chartwell Books, Inc
A division of Book Sales, Inc.
114 Northfield Avenue
Edison, New Jersey 08837

ISBN 0-7607-6464-6

Editorial and Design by
Amber Books Ltd
Bradley's Close
74–77 White Lion Street
London N1 9PF
www.amberbooks.co.uk

Project Editor: Michael Spilling
Design: Hawes Design

Printed in Singapore

PICTURE CREDITS
All artworks and photographs
© Aerospace Publishing except:
Novosti: 278.
Steve Seymour/Amber Books: 122–123,
126–127, 130–131, 168–169, 184–185,
240–241, 244–245, 252–253, 260–261,
268–269, 272–273, 285, 304–305, 308–309.
The Tank Museum, Bovington: 68, 80, 81, 84,
100, 129, 133, 137, 215, 234, 246, 247, 251,
258, 270, 271, 274, 279.
TRH Pictures: 10, 13, 24, 25, 36, 69, 72, 73,
76, 77, 85, 88, 89, 92, 93, 96, 97, 104, 105,
101, 112, 113, 116, 117, 120, 121, 124, 125,
128, 132, 136, 140, 141, 144, 145, 148, 149,
152, 153, 156, 159, 162, 166, 167, 174, 175,
178, 179, 182, 183, 186, 187, 190, 191, 194,
195, 198, 199, 202, 210, 211, 214, 218, 219,
222, 223, 226, 230, 231, 235, 238, 239, 242,
243, 250, 254, 255, 259, 262, 263, 266, 267,
275, 282, 287, 290, 291, 294, 295, 298, 299,
302, 307, 310, 311.
Jim Winchester: 163.
www.militaria-net.co.uk/hitm.htm: 108.

Contents

Introduction 6

AXIS
Germany 14
Italy 118
Japan 138

ALLIES
United States 146
United Kingdom 184
Canada 236
Soviet Union 240
France 300

Glossary 312
Index 314

INTRODUCTION

When World War II began in September 1939, the varied countries that were to unite as the Allies were equipped mainly with light tanks, generally armed with single-purpose 37mm (1.46in) guns and with armour effective only against weapons of the same calibre, if that. Only France and Russia had incorporated 75mm (2.95in) guns onto tanks, but when invasion from Germany came, they were poorly employed or simply overwhelmed by the combination of armour and air power.

GERMANY

The German panzer force was created in secret, but with Soviet cooperation after a joint AFV (armoured fighting vehicle) testing centre was set up at Kazan. Various models, called 'new model vehicle' or 'large tractor', were evaluated before the Panzer I appeared in 1934. Armed with a machine gun and intended as a training tank, it saw action in Spain, Poland and France, beside the better Panzer II. The medium and heavy equivalents

The Tiger I had the essential qualities of firepower, mobility and protection.

were the Panzer III and Panzer IV, on which many self-propelled howitzers, anti-aircraft guns and assault guns (or StuGs) were based. However, only the Panzer IV remained effective in battle throughout the war.

Germany relied on captured vehicles to guard the new territories of the Third Reich. Entire factories were captured and these, particularly in Czechoslovakia, just carried on where the previous management had left off. Czech light tanks were the basis of many 'lash-up' vehicles, mainly howitzer and anti-tank guns mounted on tank chassis.

The Soviet T-34 proved a shock to the panzer Divisions, though it was not at first encountered in quantity, barely slowing the German advance in 1941. Hitler ordered a new medium tank to counter it, with all its best features – large road wheels, wide tracks and sloped armour. The Panzer V Panther, despite a troubled debut at Kursk in July 1943, proved superior to the T-34/76. In fact, it was rarely bettered during the war. The one drawback was that production never met demand.

Germany's most famous tank was the Panzer VI, or Tiger. Mounting an 88mm (3.46in) gun, it was the heaviest tank of its day, and both reliability and mobility suffered as a result. Otherwise, the Tiger had the armour and firepower to defeat all opposition. One development was the Sturmtiger assault gun, an extraordinary weapon that appeared three years too late to be of any real value. As the fighting made its way into the city streets, German armoured vehicles operated less and less effectively. The American and British tanks were now able to get close enough for their guns to be effective against the heavier German armour.

ITALY

Italian AFV development before the war consisted mostly of two- and three-man tankettes, which were of limited use. They did play a part in the colonial campaigns of the 1930s against troops on foot or mounted on horses, and undertook garrison duties. However, against any sort of tank, anti-tank gun or artillery, they did not survive for long. Italy introduced medium tanks only in 1939, and these were burdened with cramped turrets, hull-mounted guns and riveted armour. What the Italians called medium tanks were light tanks by international standards, and their few 'heavy' tanks were equivalent to medium tanks. The P.40 heavy tank was a reasonable weapon, but few were completed by the time of the Italian armistice of 1943.

Late in the war, most medium tank production stopped. The lines were turned over to self-propelled guns; experience in North Africa with truck-mounted artillery had proved the value of mobile guns.

JAPAN

Before the war, the Japanese had made great advances in diesel engines, which worked better in cold weather and were less prone to catching fire.

Most Japanese tanks were armed with 37mm (1.46in) medium velocity guns, more effective as anti-personnel weapons than the guns of similar calibre found on other nation's tanks. However, while Allied and German armoured units began the war with mainly 37mm (1.46in) guns and ended it with weapons of 88–152mm (3.46–6in) calibre, Japan fielded nothing better than a 57mm (2.24in) gun by 1945, and then only in small quantities.

Japanese tanks did terrorize the populace in places such as Manchuria and patrolled jungle roads in Burma and the Philippines, but were never effective against Allied armour in any Pacific invasion. Only one tank per four-tank platoon was equipped with a radio, and if that was knocked out, the platoon tended to collapse in confusion. When the Soviet Union declared war on Japan in August 1945, its T-34s destroyed what little opposition the Japanese tank divisions could mount with their 37–57mm (1.46–2.24in) guns and light armour.

UNITED STATES

Tank development between the wars suffered as the military was sidelined during the Depression years. The Army disbanded its Armored Corps in the 1920s, passing all tank development to the infantry. To keep Congress from noticing the cavalry's own tank experiments, all such developments were named 'combat cars'. The last of these, the M2 combat car of 1935, led to the M2, M3 and M5 Stuart (or 'Honey') light tanks, which served throughout the war.

In 1939, the United States had only about 500 tanks, most of them obsolete models. In July 1940, having watched Hitler's panzer Divisions rampaging through Western

An M4A2 Sherman leads US infantry in an assault on a German town in 1945.

Europe, America created its Armored Force. In 1941, the first worthwhile US medium tank, the M3 (or Lee/Grant), entered service as industry geared up towards production on a massive scale. Automobile makers were enlisted, offering their expertise with production lines. In Germany, tank construction was allocated to heavy engineering firms, a fact that helps to explain why the Americans were able to produce many more tanks.

The M4 Sherman shared the suspension of the M3, but had a rotating turret with a single large gun. The Sherman is the best-known tank of World War II, and was the principal tank of the Allies from 1942. It was built in greater numbers than any tank outside the Soviet Union. The total of 48,000 Shermans and its variants exceeds the total of all German tanks, tank destroyers and assault guns produced during the war years.

Mobile and reliable, the Sherman was used in all theatres, but its armament and armour lagged behind German developments. It often took four or five Shermans to get past a single Tiger. Worse, the Sherman had a propensity to catch fire. After a long, problematic development involving many protoypes, the United States managed to field a heavy tank with 90mm (3.54in) gun in

British tanks, like the Valentine, were usually a step behind their contemporaries.

Europe in early 1945. However, the M26 Pershing was not the answer to the Tiger and Panther, and was to have more success in Korea against the T-34.

UNITED KINGDOM

At the outbreak of war, the British had the only completely mechanized army in the world, most others relying on horses (to a greater or lesser degree) for transport and

artillery towing. Nonetheless, British tank design lagged behind that of other European nations and the United States.

'Infantry' tanks, as their name suggests, were intended to work alongside the foot soldiers, particularly to lead them through breaches they made in the defences. Trench-crossing ability was valued over speed, so these tanks tended to be lengthy, often cumbersome machines with many roadwheels. One model, the Matilda II, gave valuable service in the Western Desert against the feeble Italian tanks, but when it faced the German medium tanks, particularly upgunned Panzer IIIs and the 88mm (3.46in) anti-tank gun, its day was over.

Most famous was the Churchill, which appeared in many versions from 1941. Despite a ponderous top speed of 15mph (24km/h), it played an important role in Normandy and beyond.

The 'Cruiser' tanks were faster and initially more lightly armed. They ranged from lightly armed vehicles, such as the Crusader – which were effective against the Italian but not German tanks – to the much heavier and better Centaur, Cromwell and Comet.

The British also used the M4 Sherman in large numbers, and developed mine-clearers, 'swimming' tanks, and, most importantly, the 'Firefly', which had a 76mm (17pdr) anti-tank gun shoehorned into its turret. This was the only tank in the Northwest Europe campaign able to defeat the opposition from a range that was at least reasonably safe.

Good use was made of armoured cars for reconnaissance and for hit-and-run raids. One of the best was in fact American, the T-17 Staghound, which was used only by UK and Commonwealth armies.

SOVIET UNION

The Soviet Union adopted Western ideas in the early 1930s, most importantly the Christie suspension, with its large road-wheels touching top and bottom tracks. This led directly to the BT series of fast tanks, in service in large numbers by 1941.

Soviet development produced several failures, including multi-turreted 'land battleships', but by the eve of war had produced some of the best tanks of the era. The Nazis, who had assumed they knew all they needed to know about Soviet tank development after sharing the test facility at Kazan, were astonished by the T-34, which they first encountered in June 1941.

The T-34 was superior in all the important respects – protection, firepower and mobility. Most importantly, it had sloped armour plate on the front hull and turret. A principle of ballistics is that a surface mounted at 45 degrees has twice the resistance to penetration as a vertical sheet of the same thickness. Thus the T-34 could be lighter for a given level of protection and thus faster and more agile. When the Germans countered with the Panther, the T-34 was improved. In 1944, the T34/85 was

unleashed, its armour doubled in places, and with better protection for the commander, and an excellent 85mm (3.34in) gun. This was probably the best all-round tank of the war, and was available in huge numbers – more than two-and-a-half times the number of T-34/85s were built than were Panthers.

The KV-1 heavy tank was not as good, having a more traditional suspension and less well-shaped armour. It was, however, adaptable, evolving via the KV-85 to the IS-1, IS-2 and IS-3 'Stalin' tanks, which were to influence post-war Soviet tank design.

As the war went on, the Soviet Union developed heavier and heavier self-propelled guns on existing tank chassis. Monsters such as the ISU-152 were used like wrecking balls to demolish buildings and clear a path for the foot soldiers in the centre of Germany's towns and cities.

In the offensive of 1944, the Soviets fielded enough of their heaviest IS tanks and SU guns to push back the German panzers –

even the Tigers and Panthers – across the length of the Eastern Front.

CANADA

Canada's contribution to the development of armour was the cast-construction Ram tank. In some ways superior to the M4 Sherman, with which it shared many components, the Ram saw no action as a battle tank, but many were converted to armoured personnel carriers and command post versions. Otherwise, Canada's factories produced British designs, such as the Valentine tank, in large numbers.

FRANCE

France made great strides in mechanizing its army in the 1930s and fielded a range of light, medium and heavy tanks. These shared thick, largely cast armour and good guns, but tended to be unmanoeuvrable and slow. They also relied on the commander to find targets and to aim and fire the turret gun. The

The IS-3 saw some wartime service and was a model for all post-war Soviet tanks.

Char B1 had a four-man crew, but its 75mm (2.95mm) main gun was buried within the hull, requiring the whole tank to turn to face the target. Outflanked in 1940 by the speedy German light panzers and outgunned by the five-man Panzer IV or caught in the open by dive-bombers, the French tanks were soon defeated or captured.

13

PANZER II AUSF F

*The Panzer II was the main German tank in
use in 1939. Although very lightly armed and
armoured, nearly 2000 were built. It was soon
replaced on the main fronts by heavier tanks.*

The thin armour plating was enough to
defeat the anti-tank weapons and tank
guns of the time, but the 20mm (0.78in)
gun itself was not effective against
anything but soft-skinned vehicles.

The Panzer II was armed with a
20mm (0.78in) cannon and a
7.92mm (0.31in) machine gun.

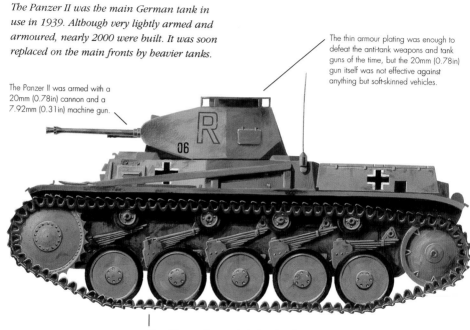

One of the more famous vehicles based on the Panzer II
was the Wespe (wasp) self-propelled howitzer.

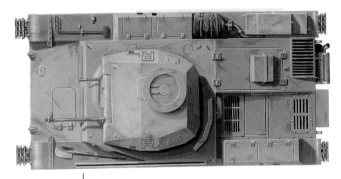

Despite their obsolescence, new Panzer II versions were produced, including flamethrower tanks, and conversions into gun carriages continued into 1943 and 1944.

The maximum armour protection on the Ausf F was 35mm (1.37in) on the upper hull. This was more than double the armour thickness of the first models.

The Ausf F was the final production model of the Panzer II, entering production in March 1941.

In the 1920s and early 1930s, the Germans, who were forbidden by the Treaty of Versailles to have any tanks, built a number of armoured fighting vehicles (AFVs) with cover names such as 'large tractor' and 'new model vehicle'. These heavy vehicles had merit, but were too large for series production given the limited engineering capacity in Germany at the time. What was needed was a light tank that would be cheap and easy to build and could

The speed and mobility of the Panzer Is and IIs contributed to the swift defeat of the French army in 1940.

serve as a training vehicle until industry recovered. A series of vehicles followed, most having a crew of two men and a single machine gun in the turret.

The Panzer II was a larger version of these early tanks with a 20mm (0.78in) cannon as the primary weapon. The Panzer II was seen as a stopgap to cover delays in the development of the Panzer III, and was intended only for training and reconnaissance use. As it happened, they were the most numerous tanks in service during the Polish campaign in 1939, and over 1200 were available during the Western

Panzer II Ausf F

Powerplant:	119kW (160hp) Maybach HL62TR six-cylinder petrol engine
Performance:	The Panzer II Ausf F had a maximum road speed of 40km/h (25mph) and a road range of 200km (125 miles)
Dimensions:	length: 4.81m (15ft 9.5in); width: 2.28m (7ft 6in); height: 2.15m (7ft)

campaign in May 1940. By this time, enough heavier tanks were in service to lead the assaults, so the Panzer Is were used in a 'reconnaissance-exploitation' role. In other words, they probed the enemy line, attacking only where the defences were weak, and calling up heavier firepower on their radios.

The Panzer II's light armament worked best against troops and light vehicles.

GERMANY

17

PANZER III AUSF H

The Panzer III was Germany's most important tank of the early war years, and it appeared with various types of armament. The Ausf H had additional armour added as a result of combat experience in Poland and France.

The Panzer III Ausf H had a new turret design with double armour thickness and a turret basket at the rear. This was retrofitted to earlier models.

The Ausf H had wider tracks and new drive sprockets and idler wheels, the latter having eight aluminium-tube spokes.

Production of the basic Panzer III models continued into July 1943, but assault guns and other derivatives were produced until May 1945.

At the time of the German invasion of the Soviet Union, there were nearly 1000 late-model Panzer IIIs available on the Eastern Front.

The Ausf H's turret was redesigned to mount the new 50mm (1.96in) KwK L/42 cannon.

Panzer IIIs with the 50mm (1.96in) gun were the most effective tank in the early part of the North African campaign, able to defeat all Allied tanks until the arrival of the Sherman.

The French campaign showed the need for more armour and this was fitted mainly as bolt-on plates on this model.

GERMANY

German re-armament plans in the 1930s required the new panzer battalions to be constituted of three light-medium tank companies and one heavy-medium company. The lighter tank that was to form the bulk of the panzer force for much of the war, remaining in production to its end, was the Panzer-kampfwagen (PzKpfw or Panzer) III.

One reason for its success was that the specification for the diameter of the turret ring allowed upgunning to weapons of a higher calibre than the 37mm (1.46in) originally fitted. Development began in 1935 and the earliest models were available by 1937, seeing service in Poland in 1939. Despite problems with the thin armour, the Panzer III defeated all opposition in the Blitzkrieg campaigns, its only significant losses coming to Polish anti-tank guns.

A Panzer III leads the assault during Operation Barbarossa, 1941.

The first four models (Ausf A, B, C, and D) differed mainly in suspension details. The Ausf E introduced the definitive six-wheel main suspension and had thicker armour, as did the Ausf F. The first mass-produced version was the Ausf G, introduced in spring 1940 – 600 were built, compared to a total of 601 for all previous versions. The Ausf H, illustrated here, was the first model to introduce heavier main armament, a 50mm (1.96in) KwK L/42 cannon, although this

Panzer III Ausf H

Powerplant:	224kW (300hp) Maybach HL120TRM V-12 petrol engine
Performance:	The Panzer III Ausf H had a maximum road speed of 40km/h (25mph) and a road range of 163km (100 miles)
Dimensions:	length: 5.41m (17ft 9 in); width: 2.95m (9ft 8in); height: 2.44m (8ft)

was also fitted to later Ausf Gs, production of which continued in parallel. In the invasion of the Soviet Union in 1941, this gun was rendered obsolete by the T-34. Subsequent models were fitted with long-barrelled 75mm (2.95in) cannon that were able to outrange Soviet tanks.

Panzergrenadiers dismount from a Panzer III in the Ukraine, 1941.

GERMANY

GERMANY

PANZER III AUSF J (SPECIAL)

*The so-called 'special' version of the Panzer III
Ausf J introduced a long-barrelled gun, which
increased the hitting power of this older tank,
much to the surprise of the Allies.*

The 50mm (1.96in) cannon
was a small calibre by 1942,
but was still able to defeat
most Allied light tanks.

The new high-velocity gun was much
harder hitting, but still unable to defeat
the frontal armour of the Soviet T-34.

Production of the Ausf J with the long gun
amounted to 1067. This compares to 1549
with the 'standard' gun.

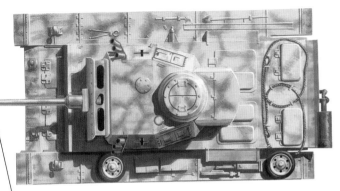

Compared to the Ausf F model, the Ausf J had a prominent turret bustle for ammunition stowage.

The new gun was 60 times as long as its diameter, or '60 calibres'. Earlier Ausf Js had a 45 calibres gun.

The Ausf J had triple smoke dischargers on the forward part of the turret.

One 7.62mm (3in) MG 34 machine gun was mounted in the upper hull and another was fitted coaxially with the main gun.

GERMANY

23

In 1942, Allied forces in North Africa encountered a Panzer III with a new long-barrelled gun. This had the same calibre as the guns fitted on the current model (Ausf J) Panzer IIIs, but it was longer, harder-hitting and much more accurate. Dubbed 'specials' by the Allies, these arrived

The Panzer III 'special' shocked the Allies when first encountered in 1942.

on battlefields just when current guns were proving inadequate. Its introduction was postponed by a rare example of German disobedience: in August 1940, Hitler saw the

Panzer III Ausf J (special)

Powerplant:	224kW (300hp) Maybach HL120TRM1 V-12 petrol engine
Performance:	The Panzer III Ausf J had a maximum road speed of 40km/h (25mph) and a road range of 155km (96 miles)
Dimensions:	length: 6.28m (20ft 7in); width: 2.95m (9ft 8in); height: 2.5m (8ft 2in)

The Ausf J (special) was an example of Hitler's interference in panzer design.

new long-barrelled (60 calibres) 50mm (1.96in) KwK 30 cannon and ordered that it be fitted to the Panzer III. The ordnance department ignored him, satisfied by the performance of the recently introduced 45 calibres gun. When the Panzer III with the big gun did not appear at his birthday parade

in April 1941, Hitler noticed and insisted again that it be fitted.

In early 1942, Ausf Js with the new gun were issued to motorized infantry detachments and to the panzer battalions that had been hard hit in late 1941 after the Soviet army regrouped.

PANZER IV AUSF F1

The Panzer IV was the standard heavy tank in German army service in 1939. Nearly 8500 were built in 10 major models.

The Panzer IV set the standard for tanks to follow, with crew and armament layout being copied by most other nations.

The device under the gun was an aerial deflector, which prevented the gun catching on the radio aerial as the turret rotated.

Side hatches on the turret allowed the gunner and loader to escape in the event that the tank was disabled.

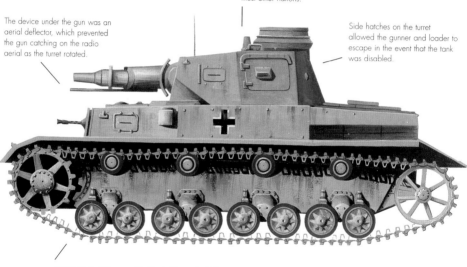

Panzer IV Ausf F2s served in North Africa, the Balkans and the Soviet Union. By mid-1943, there were almost none left on the Eastern Front.

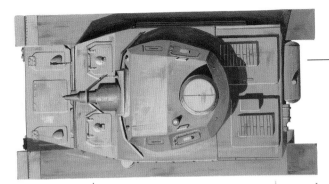

A total of 462 Ausf F1s were produced from a total of over 9000 Panzer IVs of all variants.

Later models of the Panzer IV Ausf F (usually known as Ausf F2) were fitted with the long-barrelled KwK 40 L/43 with a much higher muzzle velocity.

This early example has the original mounting for the hull machine gun. Later Ausf Fs had an armoured ball mounting.

The version illustrated is an Ausf F1 with increased armour over previous versions (up to 50mm/1.96in), a modified turret, wider tracks and intakes on the glacis plate for brake cooling.

GERMANY

27

GERMANY

The Panzer IV was developed in the mid-1930s to fulfil German army plans for the fourth 'heavy' company in the panzer divisions that were then being secretly formed by the Nazis.

In 1938, when the first examples were delivered, the only Western tanks with firepower to match it were obsolescent French models with tactically inefficient hull-mounted guns. Only 211 had been completed by the outbreak of war in September 1939.

By May 1940, there were 280 of the first four models (Ausf A–D) available to the forces poised to invade France and the Low Countries. The Panzer IV (which beat the Panzer III into production) set the pattern for battle tanks up to the present day, with a centrally mounted rotating turret mounting a heavy gun armament and a coaxial machine

A short-gun Panzer IV undergoes an engine change in a Russian village.

Panzer IV Ausf F1

Powerplant:	224kW (300hp) Maybach HL120TRM V-12 petrol engine
Performance:	The Panzer IV Ausf F1 had a maximum road speed of 42km/h (26mph) and a road range of 200km (125 miles)
Dimensions:	length: 5.92m (19ft 5in); width 2.84m (9ft 4in); height: 2.68m (8ft 7in)

A troop of Panzer IV Ausf F2s warily crosses the Russian steppe in the summer of 1943.

gun; a commander's cupola allowing 360 degree vision; a rear-mounted engine; and a forward compartment for the driver and radio operator.

Most of these features had appeared on various earlier tanks, but the impact of the German medium panzers in 1939–40 meant that almost all subsequent medium and heavy tanks have followed the same basic principles of design.

Early models were armed with the short-barrelled KwK 37 L/24 75mm (2.95in) gun, but this was outranged by the 76mm (3in) guns of the Soviet T-34s and production switched to the F2 model with a long-barrelled KwK 40 L/43 gun.

PANZER 38(T)

*The Panzer 38(t) was in production for the
Czech army when the Germans annexed most
of the country in 1939. Over 1400 were built
(or rebuilt) for German use.*

The main armament of the Panzer 38(t) was
a 37.2mm (1.46in) Skoda cannon. Two
Czech Type 37 (MG 37) machine guns
were also fitted, one in the turret and one in
the front hull.

The armour plate was
25mm (0.98in) steel on
most surfaces, held
together with large rivets.

Some later models of the Panzer 38(t) were used on the
Russian Front as parts of armoured trains.

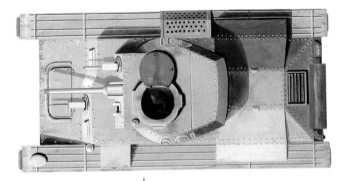

With a 37.2mm (1.46in) cannon
and two machine guns, the
Panzer 38(t) was better armed
than most German-designed tanks
of 1939.

The Panzer 38(t) was
designed for a crew
of two but was rebuilt
by the Germans for
three-man operation.

The Panzer 38(t) was a
development of the unreliable
Czech Type 35 tank. Many of
these were rebuilt and operated
by Germany.

GERMANY

A Panzer 38(t) passes despatch riders on a Russian road.

The Panzer 38(t) was one of the principal German tanks of the early war years although it was not a German design, being developed and built in Czechoslovakia. The Czech army had ordered 150 of the LT Vz 38 light tank with a 37mm (1.46in) cannon in 1938, but the German annexation of Bohemia and Moravia took place a few months later, before any deliveries could be made. The Germans took over the Praga tank factory and completed the order for themselves.

One modification they made to the Panzer 38(t) – 't' for 'Tschechoslowakisch', or Czechoslovakian – was to make space for a loader's position, lowering the commander's workload at the expense of 18 rounds of ammunition.

The first examples were designated the Ausf (Ausführung, or model) A and many served in the Polish campaign. The next versions (Ausf B, C and D) had minor changes of equipment, but were otherwise identical. The first of these models served in France, where their mobility enabled them to outflank the heavy and ponderous French tanks and penetrate their weaker side armour and tracks. After the Blitzkrieg campaigns of 1939–40, the Panzer 38(t) in its original form served on all fronts except North Africa.

Panzer 38(t)

Powerplant:	93.25kW (125hp) Praga EPA six-cylinder petrol engine
Performance:	The Panzer 38(t) had a maximum road speed of 38km/h (23.6mph) and a road range of 170km (105 miles)
Dimensions:	length: 4.54m (14ft 8in); width: 3.63m (11ft 11in); height: 2.95m (9ft 8in)

There were many adaptations of the basic chassis, including anti-aircraft tanks, tracked howitzers and self-propelled guns. During the war some were even exported to Hungary, Romania, the Slovak Free State, and even 'neutral' Sweden.

The quick and mobile Panzer 38(t) helped bolster Germany's own tank production in the late 1930s.

GERMANY

PANZER V AUSF D PANTHER

*One of the best tanks of the war, the Panther
embodied the results of combat experience and
the best features of Soviet tanks. A total of 5976
Panthers were produced over the course
of the war.*

The Panther's main gun was a 75mm
(2.95in) KwK 42 cannon with a length
of 70 calibres. The turret was
hydraulically traversed and the gun
could be elevated to 18 degrees.

The 'flame trap' exhaust mufflers at the rear
of the Panther prevented the glow from the
exhaust being visible at night and revealing
the Panther's position.

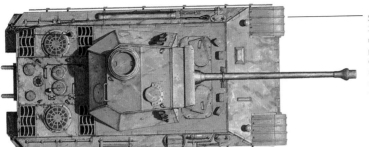

Sloping the armour at
30 degrees doubled its
resistance to armour-
piercing shells by
causing ricochets
rather than
penetration. The Panther's
turret armour was
110mm (4.33in) thick.

During production of the Panther Ausf D frontal
armour was increased from 60mm (2.36in) to
80mm (3.15mm). The thicker armour and new
features such as steel road wheels and a bow
gun appeared on the subsequent Ausf A model.

GERMANY

35

GERMANY

Although it had a disastrous combat debut, the Panther matured to become the best all-round German tank of the war. Conceived as a response to the Russian T-34, the Panther featured sloped frontal armour, wide tracks, a powerful engine and a good gun. As a result, it had good mobility, especially on rough terrain, and was available in large enough numbers

White-camouflaged troops ride a column of Panthers to the Eastern Front in the winter of 1944–45.

to make a difference in many battles. The three new features that the Panther embodied, based on Soviet practice, were large road wheels, sloped armour on all surfaces and an overhanging gun. This latter feature had been avoided on previous panzers because it restricted turret movement too much.

The first prototype was ready in September 1942 and was immediately ordered with a top priority rating – the first production Panzer V Panther Ausf D model rolled out only two months later. Several factories were put to work, reaching a peak

Panzer V Ausf G

Powerplant:	522kW (700hp) Maybach HL230P30 V-12 petrol engine
Performance:	The Panther had a maximum road speed of 46km/h (29mph) and a road range of 200km (125 miles)
Dimensions:	length: 8.86m (29ft); width: 3.4m (11ft 2in); height: 2.98m (9ft 9in)

of 330 vehicles per month during 1944. Indeed, the summer offensive in the Soviet Union was delayed until July so that enough Panthers would be ready. In the event, the Panther's rapid development had left many 'bugs' in the first machines that fought at Kursk. Suspensions broke, tracks failed and

A Panther leads troops of the Grossdeutschland division on the Eastern Front, August 1944.

GERMANY

the engines had a worrying tendency to catch fire. The survivors of these first actions were rebuilt as Panzerbefehlswagen command tanks. Another rebuilt version was the Bergepanther V, which was used to recover damaged tanks from the battlefield.

There were 350 of this turretless version. The improved Panther Ausf A, which was built from mid-1943, rectified most of these deficiencies and also featured a new glacis plate with a ball-mounted machine gun.

The definitive Ausf G, appearing in March 1944, had improved crew vision devices and thicker side armour. Some late vehicles had all-steel road wheels (which saved rubber as well as being stronger), and a number had an early infrared sighting device – technology that was well ahead of its time. The Panther comprised half the strength of the panzer divisions by mid-1944 and was active on all the fronts. About 450 took part in the Ardennes offensive in late 1944, some disguised as American tank destroyers in an effort to sow confusion in Allied ranks.

Total production was 5976 Panthers, 3126 of which were Ausf Gs, the last of these

In Normandy, the Panther was the most feared of the German tanks.

being delivered in April 1945. Only a few prototypes of the Ausf F model with a small turret and an 88mm (3.46in) gun were ever completed.

All panzer divisions had their own light and medium transport. This Panther is accompanied by a SdKfz 250 and a motorcycle with sidecar.

The Panther's Combat Debut

The German offensive at the Kursk salient was delayed until July 1943 in order to have enough Panthers available. The first units set off from the railhead for the front on 5 July. This delay contributed to the loss of the battle. Unfortunately, too, development and testing were still not complete and transmission, suspension and cooling system problems brought most of the tanks to a halt before they could even reach the battlefield. The first 250 Panthers were delivered with defective engines and were overweight. In actual combat, they were prone to catch fire when hit and its crews were also inadequately trained. Fewer than 45 were still in service just one month later.

The legendary General Heinz Guderian, then Inspector-General of the Armoured Troops, referred to the Panther as 'our problem child'. Improvements were soon at hand and the Panther went on to achieve a formidable reputation.

GERMANY

PANZER V AUSF G PANTHER

The Panther was developed through several models during the war. The definitive version was the Ausf G, which had several improvements to ease production, a new commander's cupola and the machine gun first introduced on the Ausf A. It was the most numerous Panther, and over 3100 were produced.

This Panther has an overall coating of Zimmerit anti-magnetic paste. This was vulnerable to damage, exposing the metal surface underneath.

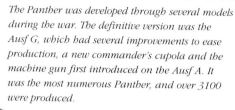

Some late Panther Gs had all-steel road wheels (which saved rubber as well as being stronger), and a number had an early infrared sighting device – technology that was well ahead of its time.

The Panther Ausf G cured most of the problems of the initial Ausf D and later Ausf A models, such as poor cooling and inadequate armour in some areas.

The Panther Ausf G was built from March 1944 and featured a new glacis plate with a ball-mounted machine gun, improved crew vision devices and thicker side armour.

GERMANY

41

PANZER VI AUSF E TIGER I

The Tiger was the most famous of all German tanks and simply had better armour and a better gun than any British or American tank it faced in 1944. It was vulnerable to air attack and could not be produced in great enough numbers to stop the Allies.

Tigers had a crew of five: commander, loader, gunner, driver and radio operator/ bow gunner.

The innovative interleaving road wheels were prone to clogging with mud, which in cold weather froze overnight and immobilized the Tiger.

Despite its capabilities, the Tiger was complex, unwieldy and vulnerable to attack from the rear.

The Tiger's wide tracks gave it a low 'footprint' and excellent cross-country manoeuvrability. On the other hand they made the tank too wide for rail transport, which required special narrow transport tracks.

GERMANY

43

GERMANY

The Tiger was the most famous of all German tanks and perhaps the most famous AFV of all time. Specifications for what was to become the Tiger were issued as early as 1937, but this 'breakthrough tank' project was cancelled after some test models were built by Henschel. In 1941 the design was dusted off when a new requirement for a heavy tank mounting an 88mm (3.46in) gun was issued. This requirement was changed at least twice before prototypes were ordered from both Henschel and Porsche, and these were to be demonstrated before Hitler on his birthday on 20 April 1942.

Both designs were quite similar and both were given production orders, as the Panzer VI Tiger and the Tiger (P) – for Porsche. The Henschel model was superior, easier to

Tigers of the 101st Heavy Battalion led the German counterattack in Normandy in 1944.

Panzer VI Ausf H Tiger I

Powerplant:	485kW (650hp) Maybach HL210P45 V-12 petrol engine
Performance:	The Tiger had a maximum road speed of 37km/h (23mph) and a road range of 117km (73 miles)
Dimensions:	length: 8.62m (27ft 9in); width: 2.82m (9ft 3in); height: 2.86m (9ft 5in)

Tigers from the 2nd SS Panzer Division move through woods in Belorussia.

produce and did not have the technical problems that dogged the Porsche tank.

Chosen for large-scale production, it was rushed into service in August 1942 to participate in the attack on Leningrad, where it was used in unsuitable terrain and soon picked out for special attention by the anti-

tank gunners. Nor was success achieved in Tunisia soon afterwards, although the design of the Tiger aroused great interest among Allied armies.

The Tiger's heyday was in Normandy after the Allied landings, when the very suggestion that there were Tigers (or even a Tiger) in the area was enough to cause 'Tiger Terror' and hold up an advance. The Tiger simply had better armour and a better gun than any British or American tank it faced in 1944.

GERMANY

45

GERMANY

A battle-worn Tiger undergoes a paint touch up on the Eastern Front.

The 88mm (3.46in) gun could penetrate the armour of a Cruiser IV at 2000m (6560ft), but the Cruiser had to get within one metre (3.28ft) to defeat the Tiger's frontal armour!

A well-handled Tiger could destroy a dozen opposing tanks in a single engagement, and if lucky, might be able to withdraw to fight again. Despite its capabilities, however, it was unwieldy and vulnerable to attack from the rear. The innovative interleaving road wheels tended to clog with mud, which often froze overnight, immobilizing the Tiger. Because the Tiger was too heavy for most smaller bridges, a snorkel could be fitted for fording rivers, although this was later omitted.

There were few variants, including the Befehlpanzer command tank and the Bergetiger recovery tank. One uncompleted version was a Rammtiger with an armoured carapace for demolishing buildings.

Because of its thick armour, the Tiger was virtually unbeatable unless ambushed and hit from close range.

Production ended in August 1944 after 1354 had been built, but Tigers fought on until the last were encircled in Berlin in May 1945.

The Tiger's Combat Debut

The Tiger appeared in battle for the first time in August 1942, when four tanks rolled off a train near Leningrad and went straight to the front lines. The Russian forces retreated in the face of the assault led by the huge new tanks, but the terrain – soft soil among forested areas – was far from ideal for the heavy and unmanoeuvrable Tigers. The gearbox of one Tiger failed, as did the engine of another. Steering problems disabled the third. Only one remained in action after the first day's fighting. The Germans managed to recover the Tigers under fire that night, but they were out of action until late September. Tigers were not available in large numbers until the winter offensive of 1942–43, at which time they accounted for a quarter of all the Russian tanks destroyed in that offensive.

GERMANY

GERMANY

PANZER VI AUSF H TIGER I

*Few changes were made in Tiger I production,
but late models had many subtle improvements,
such as steel road wheels and a Panther-type
commander's cupola with a machine gun
mount. Production of the Tiger ended in 1944
in favour of the even heavier Tiger II.*

This Tiger was covered with
Zimmerit, a paste that
hardened to insulate the metal
armour against magnetic mines
applied by Russian sappers.

The 88mm (3.46in) KwK 36 cannon was adapted
from the dual purpose 88mm (3.46in) anti-aircraft
and anti-tank gun. In the Tiger it had a new recoil
system and was electrically fired.

The Tiger was wider than previous German tanks. In order to transport it by rail, the outer road wheels were removed and narrower tracks fitted.

The Tiger had a 7.92mm (0.31in) MG 34 machine gun in the right hull front and on the gun mantlet. An anti-aircraft gun could also be fitted to the commander's cupola for anti-aircraft defence.

GERMANY

49

PANZER VI TIGER II

The King Tiger was the most powerful battle tank to enter service in World War II. It had an unbeatable combination of armour and armament and was far ahead of Allied developments. Unfortunately for Germany, too few were produced.

The Henschel turret had a massive 180mm (7in) of armour on the front face, and the front of the hull was nearly as strong at 150mm (5.9in).

The King Tiger could fire armour-piercing and high explosive shells. The internal capacity was 72 rounds.

The King Tiger used the interleaving road wheel design of the Panther and Tiger. Many other features, such as the exhausts and frontal shape, came from the Panther.

The Tiger II shared no major components with the Tiger I and in fact was more like a scaled-up Panther in some respects.

The 88mm (3.46in) KwK 43 L/71 cannon had a muzzle velocity of 1130m (3707ft) per second. It could defeat 153mm (6in) of armour at 2000m (6560ft).

The first 50 King Tigers were built with a Porsche-designed turret that had a curved front face. This created a vulnerable 'shot trap' and a Henschel-designed turret was used on most examples.

With a combat weight of 68 tonnes, (66.9 tons) the King Tiger was the heaviest battle tank to enter service during the war.

The Tiger II was the largest conventional tank of the war, outweighed only by its sibling, the Jagdtiger. Its armour and armament was superior to any Allied tank, but it was produced too late and in insufficient quantities to effect the outcome of the war. The best version of the 88mm (3.46in) gun,

Although powerful, the King Tiger was a poor use of scarce resources.

the 71-calibres KwK 43, could not be carried by the Tiger I, so a new tank was ordered. With better armour protection, this dominated the battlefield. Hitler believed that 'biggest is best', so projects such as the

Tiger II – also known as the Königstiger (King Tiger or Royal Tiger) – and the 188-tonne (185-ton) 'Maus' self-propelled gun got the go-ahead despite their impracticality and poor use of resources.

The Henschel factory turned out 489 Tiger IIs between January 1944 and March 1945. However, the new tank was not rushed to the front but went first to training units, so combat units were not fully equipped until after the Normandy landings. Most went to

Panzer VI Tiger II

Powerplant:	522kW (700hp) Maybach HL230P30 V-12 petrol engine
Performance:	The King Tiger had a maximum road speed of 35km/h (22mph) and a road range of 170km (105 miles)
Dimensions:	length: 10.3m (33ft 11in); width: 3.76m (12ft 4in); height: 3.08m (10ft 1in)

independent tank detachments of the army and the SS, causing a stir in the Ardennes campaign before running out of fuel. The same fate befell most of these giants – at least, those that did not break down. Some were destroyed by air attack, and a few by other tanks.

The King Tiger was too heavy and wide for many roads and most bridges.

GERMANY

53

SDKFZ 232 (8-RAD)

*The German Army made much use of
armoured cars for reconnaissance during
the war and one of their best-known vehicles
was the eight-wheeled SdKfz 232 (8-rad),
or 'Achtrad'.*

In order to report their discoveries to panzer
and other units, the 232 'Achtrads' were
fitted with a large frame aerial for a
powerful medium-range radio set, and this
distinguished it from the otherwise identical
SdKfz 231 (8-rad).

The 232 (8-rad) was
armed with a 20mm
(0.78in) KwK 30
cannon and a
coaxial MG 34
machine gun.

The 231 and 232 eight-wheeled cars could
cross a trench up to 1.5m (4ft 11in) wide
and ford rivers up to 1m (3ft 3in) deep.

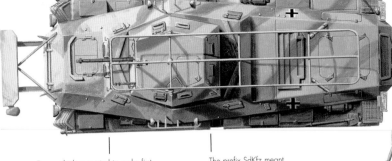

For a vehicle expected to make first contact with the enemy, the 'Achtrads' were inadequately armed and armoured. The ability to change direction (the requirement was to do so in under 10 seconds) can be understood in this light.

The prefix SdKfz meant Sonderkraftfahrzeug, or 'special purpose vehicle', and was used for half-tracks, armoured cars and tank destroyers.

The SdKfz 232 (8-rad) was an excellent off-road vehicle, partly because of its complicated but efficient all-wheel steering and differential system that prevented the inner wheels dragging in turns.

GERMANY

55

An early model 'Achtrad' demonstrates its cross-country mobility in trials.

Germany was an early exponent of armoured cars, partly because they were not tanks and therefore restricted by the Versailles Treaty. They were also a cheap and quick way to mechanize the army and give industry experience of building vehicles to military specifications.

The multi-wheeled armoured cars came out of studies using trucks with a drive on four rear wheels for good cross-country performance. Trucks could be converted, given new armoured bodies and a second steering position at the rear. Movement in either direction (as opposed to reversing) was specified for armoured cars in 1927. Six-wheeled cars entered service in 1932, but performed poorly over uneven ground, so eight-wheelers were developed. The most important of these in the early war years was the Panzerspähwagen SdKfz 232 (8-rad). For some reason, the ordnance department of the German army gave the same number to both six- and eight-wheel armoured cars, so the eight-wheeler was suffixed '8-rad' to

SdKfz 232 (8-rad)

Powerplant:	112kW (150hp) Büssing-NAG L8V V-8 petrol engine
Performance:	The SdKfz 232 (8-rad) had a maximum road speed of 85km/h (53mph) and a road range of 300km (186 miles)
Dimensions:	length: 8.86m (29ft); width: 2.2m (7ft 3in); height: 2.35m (7ft 8in) without masts

distinguish it from the 'other' 232, a 6x6 configuration vehicle. Issued to the heavy platoons of the armoured car reconnaissance squadrons, the 231s and 232s operated with other vehicles, providing fire support when needed. The 607 that were produced saw service on all fronts.

The crew of a SdKfz 232 (8-rad) mount up in Poland in 1939.

GERMANY

SDKFZ 251

The world's first purpose-designed armoured personnel carrier, the SdKfz 251 was used on all fronts and for numerous purposes from mobile howitzer to anti-aircraft gun platform. It was the most numerous German armoured vehicle ever built.

The SdKfz 251 had its own armament of a fixed MG 34 machine gun, but there was also a mount for the infantry squad's machine gun.

The sloping of the armoured plates improved the ballistic protection they offered.

Armour was only 14.5mm (0.57in), which was adequate against small arms and shell splinters.

The interleaving road wheels was a feature later used on the Panther and Tiger battle tanks.

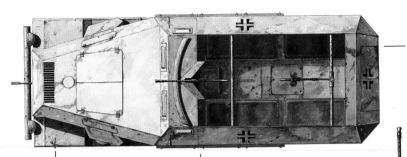

There was a rear entry door for the main compartment, but the crew often embarked and disembarked by climbing over the sides.

Later models had simplified hull construction to speed production, notably all-welded armour as opposed to mainly riveted plates.

The standard personnel carrier version could carry 10 fully equipped troops and a crew of two.

WH-816 297

Over 15,000 vehicles in the series were built, more than half of them in 1944.

When the Panzer Divisions were formed in the 1930s, it was realized that the support troops and Panzergrenadiers would be left behind unless given armoured transport into battle. The half-tracked vehicle, which was developed in France in the 1920s, evoked

Wehrmacht troops dismount from a SdKfz 251 'battle taxi' in Russia in the summer of 1942.

interest, and the firm of Hanomag was instructed to design an armoured half-track based on its earlier SdKfz 11 artillery tractor.

SdKfz 251

Powerplant:	75kW (100hp) Maybach HL42 TUKRM six-cylinder petrol engine
Performance:	The SdKfz 251 had a maximum road speed of 53km/h (33mph) and a road range of 180km (112 miles)
Dimensions:	length: 5.8m (19ft); width: 2m (6ft 7in); height: 1.75m (5ft 9in)

The Flammpanzerwagen had a 700-litre flame fuel tank.

From this came the special purpose vehicle (Sonderkraftfahrzeug) SdKfz 251, often known as the Hanomag half-track. Entering production in June 1939, it was available for the French campaign and helped maintain the momentum of the Blitzkrieg. Until they invented their own armoured personnel carriers, other nations' troops rode into battle on the back of tanks, or in trucks.

The 251 was used in all theatres of war, in many variants. The 251/1 was fitted with wooden racks for 320mm (12.6in) infantry support rockets, a weapon sometimes known as the 'Stuka on foot'. The 251/16 had dual flamethrower guns. The 251/20 had a large infrared searchlight and was used in conjunction with the IR night sights on some Panther tanks. The 251/22 was a tank destroyer version with a 75mm (2.95in) PaK 40 anti-tank gun.

GERMANY

61

SdKfz 234/2 Puma

The Puma was a fast and well armed armoured
car used for reconnaissance ahead of the main
force. There were several variants built in small
numbers – the 234/2 had a fully enclosed
armoured turret.

The Puma's main armament was a 50mm
(1.96in) KwK 39/1 cannon. There was
space inside the vehicle for 55 rounds of
ammunition.

Unlike almost all other German armoured
vehicles, the Puma had a diesel engine,
which was less likely to catch fire if
damaged.

The Pumas were all-wheel drive and all-wheel steering
(necessary to prevent the rear wheels dragging in the
turn), an advantage for a reconnaissance vehicle that
was designed to observe and report as fast as possible.

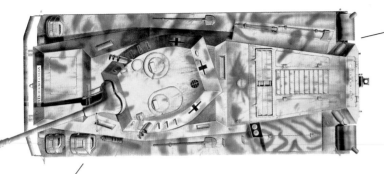

The Puma had a second backward-facing driving position ahead of the engine. This, together with a gearbox with six forward and six reverse gears, enabled the Puma to be driven equally fast in either direction

The gun mantlet provided extra ballistic protection and was of the 'Saukopf' (sow's head) variety fitted to many late-war German vehicles.

The turret was hand rotated and could be elevated from 10 degrees down to 20 degrees up.

WH-1542410

The small numbers of Pumas built (101) were distributed to four Panzer divisions and used in Russia and in western Europe.

GERMANY

63

GERMANY

The Germans used wheeled armoured cars for reconnaissance in particular. The best was the eight-wheeled SdKfz 234 series, which combined high speed, long range, and in later variants, big hitting power for its size. The SdKfz 234/2, or Puma as it became known, developed

A factory-fresh Puma is seen attracting a great deal of attention.

from earlier eight-wheeled vehicles, but was of monocoque construction, its hull forming the chassis. A fully enclosed turret was fitted, designed originally for the abandoned

Leopard light tank, and this carried a long-barrelled 50mm (1.96in) cannon that could defeat most enemy reconnaissance vehicles, the Puma's most common opponent. Development was protracted as it was intended for use in North Africa, but that campaign was over by the time problems with 'tropicalizing' the vehicle had been solved.

The first vehicles served on the Eastern Front, where their range proved invaluable, though they were complex to maintain, particularly when far from maintenance

SdKfz 234/2 Puma

Powerplant:	164kW (220hp) Tatra 103 V-12 diesel engine
Performance:	The Puma had a maximum road speed of 53mph (85km/h) and a road range of 550km/h (350mph)
Dimensions:	length: 6.8m (22ft 4in); width: 2.33m (7ft 7in); height: 2.38m (7ft 10in)

depots. The heavy main armament also encouraged Puma crews to engage the enemy, thus defeating the original purpose. Only 101 turreted 234/2 Pumas were built, followed by similar numbers of 234/3s and 234/4s, which mounted various anti-tank guns in open-topped superstructures.

This Puma was knocked out when hit on its wheels by an anti-tank weapon.

GERMANY

SDKFZ 135/1 LORRAINE SCHLEPPER

The Lorraine Schlepper was a French general-purpose weapons carrier and tug that was adapted by the German Army to provide a self-propelled heavy howitzer.

The main armament of the SdKfz 135/1 was a 150mm (5.9in) sFH 13 howitzer, the German designation for captured French weapons dating from World War I.

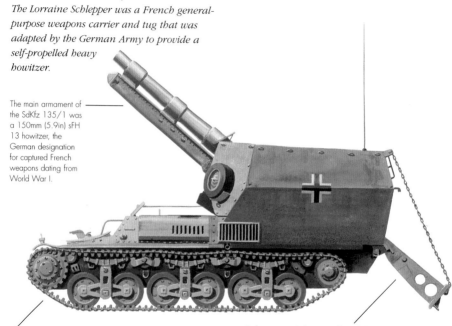

A Schlepper was a tug or gun tractor and French vehicles of this type were used as the basis of the SdKfz135/1.

At the rear was a large recoil spade that dug into the earth when the gun fired. Vehicles overhauled in 1944 incorporated the larger spade seen here, which could be raised and lowered without the crew having to leave the fighting compartment.

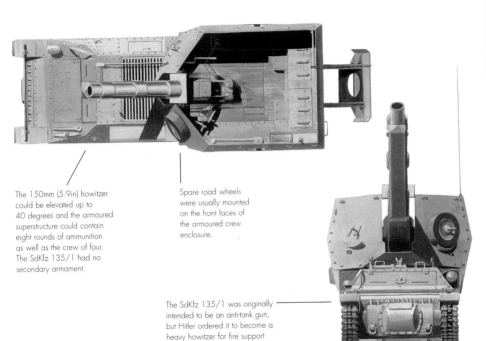

The 150mm (5.9in) howitzer could be elevated up to 40 degrees and the armoured superstructure could contain eight rounds of ammunition as well as the crew of four. The SdKfz 135/1 had no secondary armament.

Spare road wheels were usually mounted on the front faces of the armoured crew enclosure.

The SdKfz 135/1 was originally intended to be an anti-tank gun, but Hitler ordered it to become a heavy howitzer for fire support missions

GERMANY

67

One of several 'lash-ups' developed as a mobile anti-tank gun was the Lorraine Schlepper, which was based on captured French chassis combined with a World War I artillery piece. The German haul of equipment after France fell in 1940 included over 300 Tracteur Blinde

Here, a Lorraine Schlepper variant is lined up with a couple of Panthers and other German AFVs.

37Ls, which were tracked general-purpose carriers similar to the British Universal (Bren) carrier.

Withdrawn from stockpile in 1942 for the Panzerjäger project, 40 were converted on Hitler's orders to carry a 15cm (5.9in) howitzer for operations with the 21st Panzer Division of Rommel's Afrika Korps.

Most were converted in Paris using superstructures supplied by the Alkett company, but at least 30 were converted at Krefeld. About 12 were fitted with the

SdKfz 135/1 Lorraine Schlepper

Powerplant:	52.2kW (70hp) Delahaye 103TT six-cylinder petrol engine
Performance:	The SdKfz 135/1 had a maximum road speed of 34km/h (21.1mph) and a road range of 135km (84 miles)
Dimensions:	length: 5.31m (17ft 5in); width: 1.83m (6ft); height: 2.23m (7ft 4in)

10.5cm (4.1in) leFH 18/40 howitzer, and one was fitted with a Russian 122mm (4.8in) howitzer and incorporated in an armoured train that was captured in late 1944. It is believed that 94 Lorraine Schleppers were produced with the 15cm (5.9in) gun.

The cumbersome Lorraine Schlepper mounted a very heavy gun on a lightweight chassis.

GERMANY

STURMGESCHÜTZ III AUSF G

The Sturmgeschütz (StuG) assault guns were designed to provide mobile support for infantry battalions. Later models, such as the StuG III, were also used in the anti-tank role, but were not ideal.

In 1944, a coaxial machine gun was finally added, as was a remote-controlled gun for the turret roof.

The StuG III was also designated the 7.5cm Sturmgeschütz 40, the gun being 40 times the length of its calibre of 75mm (2.95in).

This Ausf G has a coating of Zimmerit anti-magnetic mine paste in a 'waffle' pattern.

Side skirts and Zimmerit coating were factory-applied to later production examples.

The StuGs were built on the chassis of the Panzer III medium tank with an all-new superstructure.

This StuG has a pair of spare road wheels mounted behind the engine deck at the rear.

The main gun had a limited range of movement – 10 degrees left and right, and 6 degrees down to 20 degrees up.

The StuG III Ausf G introduced a machine gun with shield mounted in front of the loader's hatch.

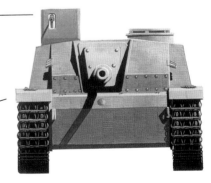

The early StuGs had no secondary armament and the Ausf F had a machine gun stowed inside that had to be brought out and fired from an exposed position.

GERMANY

The Sturmgeschütz (StuG) III Ausf G was the last in a series of 75mm (2.95in) assault guns based on the Panzer III. These began with the Ausf A of 1940 and went through four major variants before the definitive Ausf G left the factory in December 1942. Models up to the Ausf E had a short-barrelled (24 calibres) gun, but the F and G toted a 48 calibres gun with muzzle brake to counter the Soviet KV-1 and T-34. This gun developed from the PaK 40

StuGs often sported extra armoured screens or 'skirts'.

Sturmgeschutz III Ausf G

Powerplant:	224kW (300hp) Maybach HL120TRM V-12 petrol engine
Performance:	The StuG III Ausf G had a maximum road speed of 40km/h (25mph) and a road range of 155km (96 miles)
Dimensions:	length: 6.77m (22ft 3in); width: 2.95m (9ft 8in); height: 2.16m (7ft 2in)

A StuG III of the SS Leibstandarte Division is seen in Russia in early 1943.

towed anti-tank gun and signalled a change in role for the StuGs. They were designed for building assault alongside infantry, but tank production had not kept up with losses on the Eastern Front, and they now operated with panzers in conventional tank engagements. The Ausf G featured a cupola with periscopes to protect the commander as he surveyed the terrain and slanted plates protecting the front of the side panniers.

The reliability of the StuGs meant that they were employed throughout the war, adapted to other uses, such as flame-throwers and ammunition carriers. This is reflected in the production figures; 8587 StuG IIIs were built, as well as over 800 earlier versions.

GERMANY

73

PANZERJÄGER IV NASHORN

*The Nashorn ('Rhinoceros') was one of several
German 'lash-up' mobile guns. It was fast with
a powerful main gun, but vulnerable to almost
all enemy weapons above rifle calibre.*

Secondary armament was a bipod-mounted
MG 34 machine gun, stowed internally
along with 600 rounds of ammunition.

The Nashorn/Hornisse mounted
the famous PaK 43 88mm
(3.46in) cannon, also adapted
for the Tiger and Panther tanks.

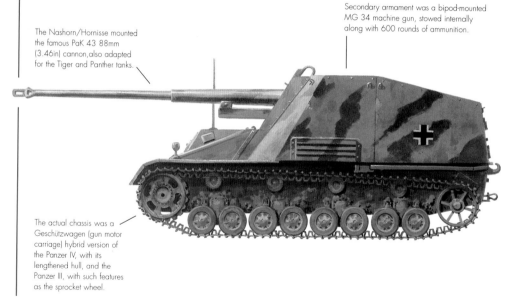

The actual chassis was a
Geschützwagen (gun motor
carriage) hybrid version of
the Panzer IV, with its
lengthened hull, and the
Panzer III, with such features
as the sprocket wheel.

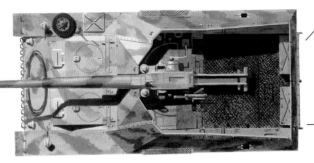

Doors at the rear allowed the ammunition to be replenished in combat. Very little could be carried inside the vehicle itself.

The open-topped hull provided little weather or battle protection for the gun crew.

The Nashorn's gun had 30 degrees of lateral traverse and could be elevated to 20 degrees.

The frontal armour was sloped at 37 degrees which increased its effectiveness, although at only 10mm (0.39in) thick it was useless against any type of armour-piercing ammunition.

GERMANY

The 88mm PaK 43 dual anti-tank/anti-aircraft gun was one of the best all-round weapons of the war, but it was hardly mobile. The invasion of the Soviet Union required artillery that could keep up with the rapid advance. The first successful attempt to self-propel the 'eighty-eight' was the 'Nashorn' (rhinoceros) Panzerjäger (tankhunter) IV, based on the Panzer IV chassis. It featured

The Nashorn's high profile made it vulnerable if caught in the open.

a new, lightly armoured superstructure in place of the gun turret with room for a gun crew of four. The engine was moved from the rear to the front to allow a larger fighting compartment. The thickest armour was on the front hull and was only 30mm steel. The gunners were only protected by 10mm armour.

Produced from February 1943 and ready in time for the summer offensives, they were issued to schwere (heavy) independent Panzerjäger detachments, which had a 'fire-brigade' role to move about the front repelling outbreaks of Soviet armour. There was a single order for 500 vehicles and 494 were completed by March 1945.

This Nashorn was captured and evaluated by the US after the war.

Panzerjäger IV Nashorn

Powerplant:	224kW (300hp) Maybach HL120TRM1 V-12 petrol engine
Performance:	The Nashorn had a maximum road speed of 42km/h (26mph) and a road range of 215km (133 miles)
Dimensions:	length: 8.44m (27ft 8in); width: 2.86m (9ft 5in); height: 2.65m (8ft 8in)

GERMANY

77

PANZERJÄGER TIGER (P) ELEFANT

Based on the Porsche Tiger, the Elefant (also known as the Ferdinand) was a purpose-built tank hunter. It was effective in its role but, like the Porsche Tiger, over-complex and unreliable, prone to breakdowns.

In late 1943, the surviving 48 vehicles were rebuilt at the factory and were fitted with a bow MG 34 machine gun for self-defence, a commander's cupola and Zimmerit anti-magnetic coating.

The long gun was supported by a travel lock when the Elefant was on the move.

The Porsche Tiger never entered service, but formed the basis of a number of vehicles. It lacked the interleaving road wheels of the Henschel Tiger.

Elefants with no secondary armament were vulnerable to infantry armed with magnetic mines and other charges. An escort of Panzer-grenadiers was deemed essential for close-range defence.

The main armament was the 88mm (3.46in) PaK 43/2 cannon. There was no secondary armament on Elefants when they were delivered.

The hull structure of the Elefant was basically the same as that of the Porsche Tiger but with 100mm (3.93in) plates bolted to the front, giving a total of 200mm (7.87in) frontal armour protection

The combat weight of 29.4 tonnes (29 tons) made the Elefant one of the heaviest German vehicles of the war.

GERMANY

79

The Elefant tank destroyer fell somewhere between earlier lightly armoured 'lash-up' designs, such as the Nashorn, and the successful Panther-based Jagdpanther. Based on the Porsche Tiger design (and initially known as

With no secondary armament on early models, the Elefant was vulnerable to attack by infantry with mines.

Ferdinand after Ferdinand Porsche), the Elefant was one of the first German vehicles to carry the long-barrelled 88mm (3.46in) flak gun. The full designation of this gun was the PaK 43/2 L/71, the suffix indicating that it was 71 calibres long.

In February 1943, Hitler ordered that 90 of these vehicles (given the ordnance number SdKfz 184) be produced and delivered to the Eastern Front. This meant abbreviating the test programme and the first were delivered by the end of May 1943, in time for the spring offensive.

Panzerjäger Tiger (P) Elefant

Powerplant:	Twin 224kW (300hp) Maybach HL120TRM V-12 petrol engines
Performance:	The Elefant had a maximum road speed of 20km/h (12.5mph) and a road range of 153km (95 miles)
Dimensions:	Length: 8.13m (26ft 8in); width: 3.36m (11ft 1in); height: 2.98m (9ft 10in)

Many of these Elefants fought at Kursk, where they were able to defeat all types of Soviet tank, but they lacked cross-country mobility and were prone to breakdowns. Many rebuilt Elefants saw further service on the Italian front, but proved unsuitable for the poor road conditions there and suffered from a lack of spare parts.

The Elefant was overly complex and consequently unsuccessful.

GERMANY

LEICHTE FELDHAUBITZE 18/2 AUF FAHRGESTELL PANZERKAMPFWAGEN II

The Wespe self-propelled howitzer was a popular and effective mobile field gun. The full name of the Wespe was the Leichte Feldhaubitze 18/2 auf Fahrgestell Panzer II (light 18/2 field gun on Panzer II chassis)

Self-protection weapons were limited to a single MG 42 machine gun supplied with each vehicle, which could be mounted in various positions.

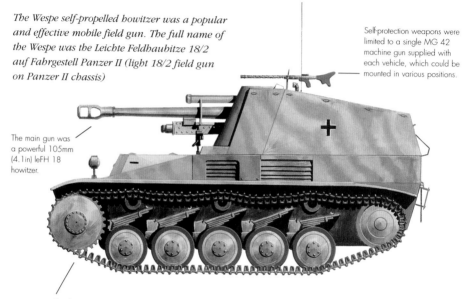

The main gun was a powerful 105mm (4.1in) leFH 18 howitzer.

The driver sat in an enclosed position at the front of the vehicle while the other four crewmen travelled and fought in the main fighting compartment.

There was room within the superstructure for a respectable 32 rounds of ammunition, but the munitions carrier version could carry 90 and was an essential adjunct if the Wespe was to carry out sustained operations.

The driver sat behind a hinged armoured hatch, which was usually propped open for driving outside the battle zone.

The open superstructure of the Wespe was protected only by slightly sloped 20mm (0.78in) steel plate. This was effective against light weapons and shell splinters, but not against direct hits from heavy weapons.

GERMANY

The Wespe provided handy mobile artillery support to panzer divisions on the Eastern Front.

The Panzer III/IV chassis was seen by the German army ordnance department as a suitable mount for a 105mm (4.1in) gun in early 1942.

When the gun was found to work satisfactorily on a Panzer II chassis, all Panzer II production was turned over to the new vehicle, a light field howitzer (leichte feldhaubitze) with the popular name 'Wespe' (wasp).

Compared to the Panzer II, the Wespe was slightly lengthened, its engine repositioned forward and with three rather than four return rollers in the suspension. The main armament could be used in a direct fire role but normally was elevated (up to 42 degrees) to provide indirect support fire.

In February 1943, 1000 were ordered, but only 835 were built. Another 159 were produced as specialist ammunition carriers. These vehicles could be converted back to Wespes in the field, using the guns from disabled vehicles.

Like many German AFVs, the Wespe was delivered in numbers in time for the 1943 summer offensive on the Eastern Front and made its debut at Kursk. More successful than many heavier self-propelled guns, it was speedy, reliable and popular with the troops.

Accordingly, it saw service on both the Eastern and Western Fronts and in Italy until the end of the war. One disadvantage was the open-topped superstructure, which gave no

Leichte Feldhaubitze 18/2 auf Fahrgestell Panzerkampfwagen II

Powerplant:	104kW (140hp) Maybach HL62TR inline six-cylinder petrol engine
Performance:	The Wespe had a maximum road speed of 40km/h (25mph) and a road range of 220km (138 miles)
Dimensions:	length: 4.81m (15ft 7in); width: 2.28m (7ft 5in); height: 2.3m (7ft 6in)

protection to crews against the elements, mortar shells or hand grenades. The same basic concept was used on the Hummel (bumble bee) self-propelled gun, based on the Panzer IV chassis.

The gun of this Wespe has been elevated to provide indirect fire on a distant target.

GERMANY

85

STURMPANZER IV BRUMMBÄR

Based on the reliable Panzer IV, the Brummbär (Grizzly Bear) was a heavily armoured mobile howitzer. However, it lacked self-defence and was useless in combat with other armoured vehicles.

The Brummbär's main weapon was a 150mm (5.9in) StuH assault howitzer firing high explosive shells.

The large superstructure housed a crew of five and nearly 40 rounds of 150mm (5.9in) ammunition.

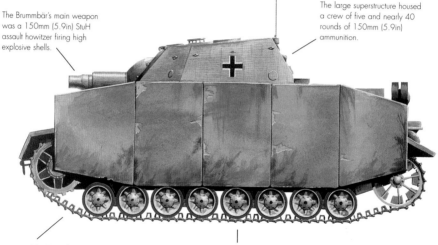

The Brummbär weighed 28 tonnes (27.5 tons), over 5 tonnes (4.9 tons) more than a standard Panzer IV Ausf G.

The vast majority of Brummbärs were built from new, with only eight converted from existing Panzer IV Ausf G tanks.

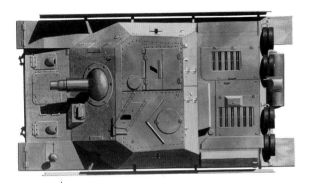

The final models remedied the deficiencies in self-defence by adding a ball-mounted machine gun in the upper-left of the front face. A commander's cupola with an MG 42 for anti-aircraft defence was another late addition.

Late production Brummbärs had a periscope for the driver, as seen here, rather than a direct-vision visor.

After 1943, armoured Schürzen ('skirts') were usually fitted, as seen here. This was simply 5mm (0.19in) mild-steel boilerplate attached by brackets to protect the hull against hollow-charge weapons, ensuring that they expended their energy well clear of the interior.

GERMANY

The Sturmpanzer IV was a variation on the Panzer IV, offering mobile artillery support to infantry. It was designed by the Alkett firm to mount a 15cm (5.96in) howitzer, and when Hitler saw the plans in October 1942 he ordered 40–60 to be built at once. These were completed in

A Brummbär and its crew head a line-up of German AFVs.

May 1943, and the series then went into production; 298 had been built by the war's end. The box-like superstructure housed a Sturmhaubitze (assault howitzer) L/12 in a

Sturmpanzer IV Brummbär

Powerplant:	224kW (300hp) Maybach HL120TRM V-12 petrol engine
Performance:	The Brummbär had a maximum road speed of 40km/h (25mph) and a road range of 210km (130 miles)
Dimensions:	length: 5.93m (19ft 5in); width: 2.88m (9ft 5in); height: 2.52m (8ft 3in)

The Brummbär was barely able to defend itself in close combat.

ball mount with frontal armour of 100mm (3.93in) and side armour of 50mm (1.96in).

Assault tank battalion 216 was the first to be equipped with the SdKfz 166 Brummbär ('Grizzly Bear'), which debuted at Kursk in July 1943. A lack of guns was a disadvantage, but the mechanical reliability and soundness of its chassis let it outclass newer designs, many of which could not outmanoeuvre the enemy or just broke down. That said, the Brummbär was heavy and slow – not a problem if firing against fixed positions at the front of an infantry assault, but a liability in defensive fighting or against enemy armour. After Kursk, three more battalions were equipped with the Brummbär and fought in Italy and in Western Europe.

89

JAGDPANZER IV/70

The Jagdpanzer IV was a tank hunter built on the chassis of the Panzer IV with a new low-profile welded superstructure, which was more suitable for ambush tactics.

Frontal armour on the IV/70 was increased from 60mm (2.36in) to 80mm (3.14in) and from 30mm (1.2in) to 40mm (1.5in) on the sides.

The original Jagdpanther IV had a 48 calibres PaK 39 cannon, The Jagdpanther IV/70 had a 70 calibre PaK 42, also firing 70mm (2.75in) shells.

The main gun could be traversed 10 degrees side to side, 5 degrees down and 15 degrees up.

The mesh side skirts could be threaded with foliage to provide camouflage when hiding in hedgerows.

The IV/70 was nearly 3 tonnes (2.9 tons) heavier than the early models, but apart from its gun was otherwise very similar.

The Jagdpanzer IV/70 was extremely nose heavy, which caused many failures of the rubber-tyred road wheels. New steel wheels were fitted on the first two bogies to remedy this problem.

Most Jagdpanzers were equipped with 'skirts' (Schürzen), which protected the vulnerable running gear. The mesh screens here would detonate an anti-tank rocket away from the hull.

GERMANY

When production of StuG III assault guns was halted by the bombing of the Alkett factory in late 1943, Hitler ordered that the StuG superstructure be fitted to the Panzer IV chassis. Already trialled, this configuration had not been

The Jagdpanzer IV employed ambush tactics in the Normandy hedgerows.

adopted due to other demands on Panzer production. At the same time Vomag, one of the Panzer IV constructors, presented a

The low profile of the Jagdpanzer IV/70 was one of its best features.

Jagdpanzer IV/70

Powerplant:	224kW (300hp) Maybach HL120TRM V-12 petrol engine
Performance:	The Jagdpanzer IV had a maximum road speed of 35km/h (22mph) and a road range of 210km (130 miles)
Dimensions:	length: 8.5m (27ft 11in); width: 3.17m (10ft 5in); height: 1.85m (6ft 1in)

design for a tank destroyer based on this chassis. Both vehicles went into production, as the StuG IV and the Jagdpanzer IV respectively. The Jagdpanzer IV featured a new superstructure with sloping surfaces and periscopes, and the vehicle's ballistic shape had few weaknesses. The original main weapon was a 75mm (2.95in) PaK 39 with a barrel 48 calibres long and this was supported by two front-mounted machine guns. The improved version, the Jagdpanzer IV/70, had a gun with a barrel 70 calibres

long – the PaK 42. Installed on Hitler's orders, it increased muzzle velocity and thus armour penetration.

The Jagdpanzer IV was a well-liked tank destroyer, which destroyed many Soviet tanks in 1944–45. However, the big gun on later models damaged its cross-country handling, slowing it down. By the time these were in action, all combat was defensive and the tank's attributes mattered little any more.

GERMANY

SDKFZ 173 JAGDPANTHER

*Unlike earlier German tank destroyers that were
modifications of existing chassis, the
Jagdpanther was designed around the best
available vehicle, the Panther heavy tank.*

The Jagdpanther had
a combat weight of
46 tonnes (45.2 tons)
and was operated by
a five-man crew.

Sloping the armour plate at the front of the
vehicle doubled its effectiveness for a given
thickness against enemy tank fire.

Side armour skirts, or
Schürzen, were often
added in service to
protect the return roller
wheels from anti-tank
rockets as seen here.

Although based on the Panther Ausf G chassis, the
Jagdpanther shared only the running gear and the
general layout of components.

94

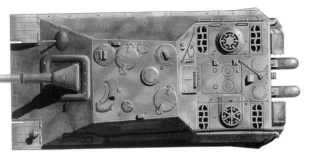

The main armament was the PaK 43/4 anti-tank cannon. A 7.92mm (0.3in) MG 34 machine gun fired from a barbette on the right of the glacis plate.

The Jagdpanther was heavily armoured. Frontal armour was 80mm (3.1in) steel, on the sides 60mm (2.3in), and on the gun mantlet a massive 120mm (4.7in).

Service entry was in June 1944 with the 559th and 654th Panzerjäger battalions, although the former only ever received enough vehicles to equip one company.

GERMANY

95

GERMANY

The Jagdpanther was one of the most effective tank destroyers built during World War II, although it never appeared on the battlefield in large enough numbers to be decisive.

The Jagdpanther was designed in 1943 to make use of the best chassis available – that of the Panther. The result, first demonstrated to Hitler in October 1943, was an unaltered Panther chassis and running gear, to which was added a new sloped-front super-structure housing a PaK 43 88mm (3.46in) anti-tank gun in a limited-traverse mount.

Initially designated Panzerjäger Panther, it was redesignated on Hitler's orders Jagdpanther (Hunting Panther) in February 1944. Production began in that month using the Panther Ausf G as the basis, but with a stronger gearbox originally intended for the

The sloped front face of the Jagdpanther gave effective protection against armour-piercing shells.

unbuilt Panther II. Production and delivery problems, including that caused by Allied bombing of the factories, meant that there were few occasions when the Jagdpanthers were able to concentrate in strength.

An exception was the Battle of the Bulge in December 1944, when they knocked out Allied tanks on a scale out of all proportion to their numbers. When the weather finally cleared over the Ardennes, many Jagdtigers were destroyed by rocket-firing fighter-bombers. Each Jagdpanther lost was an asset that could not be replaced as the factories were overrun.

Production ceased in April 1945 with the 382nd vehicle, and the last Jadgpanthers fought on until they were knocked out or until fuel supplies dried up.

The Jadgpanther was one of Germany's best armoured vehicles, but appeared too late in the war and in insufficient numbers.

SdKfz 173 Jagdpanther

Powerplant:	522kW (700hp) Maybach HL230P30 V-12 petrol
Performance:	The Jagdpanther had a maximum road speed of 46km/h (29mph) and a road range of 160km (100 miles)
Dimensions:	length: 9.9m (32ft 5in); width: 3.42m (11ft 2in); height: 2.72m (8ft 11in)

GERMANY

97

SDKFZ 140 LEICHTE FLAKPANZER 38(T)

The Leichte Flakpanzer 38(t) light anti-aircraft tank was one of numerous specialized modifications of the Czech-built LT Vz 38 tank that was used in large numbers by German forces. It was too lightly armed to be much use in the anti-aircraft role, but had a limited secondary role against soft-skinned vehicles and troops.

The only armament was the standard German light anti-aircraft (Flak) gun of World War II, the 20mm (0.78in) Flak 38.

The high mount allowed the 20mm (0.78in) gun to be depressed to five degrees below the horizontal, at least in the forward arc. The gun could be elevated to 90 degrees.

Armour plating on the new superstructure was only 10mm (0.39in) thick with another 10mm (0.39in) on the gun shield.

Other modifications of the basic Panzer 38(t) included ammunition carriers, the Marder mobile anti-tank gun and the Grille 150mm (5.9in) self-propelled howitzer.

GERMANY

99

B ased on the versatile Czech-built Panzer 38(t) chassis, the Leichte Flakpanzer (light anti-aircraft tank) was the first fully tracked self-propelled anti-aircraft vehicle produced in the war. It was developed as a makeshift solution to the urgent need for anti-aircraft support for the Panzer regiments on the Eastern Front after

The Leichte Flakpanzer 38(t) was too lightly armed to be a very effective anti-aircraft vehicle, and was soon made obsolete by the development of better anti-aircraft vehicles.

Hitler refused to allow Panzer IVs to be fitted with a powerful quadruple 20mm (0.78in) mount.

The 37mm (1.46in) gun turret of the standard Panzer 38(t) was replaced by a rear-mounted octagonal shield made of 10mm (0.39in) armour plate. The upper portions of the gun shield hinged outwards and were opened up when the gun was in action, for better access to the gun and for traverse against targets at low angles. The gun was traversed by hand and was supplied with up to 360 rounds of ammunition stored within the vehicle.

Some 150 SdKfz 140 Leichte Flakpanzers were ordered in the winter of 1943, but only 140 were converted after the vehicle's lack

SdKfz 140 Leichte Flakpanzer 38(t)

Powerplant:	93kW (123hp) Praga EPA Model I six-cylinder petrol engine
Performance:	The Leichte Flakpanzer had a maximum road speed of 42km/h (28mph) and a road range of 250km (155 miles)
Dimensions:	length: 4.61m (15ft 1in); width 2.15m (7ft 1in); height: 2.25m (7ft 5in)

of firepower proved disappointing and newer vehicles were developed, which had dual and quadruple mounts (such as the Flakpanzer IV Wirbelwind).

Issued to the flak platoons of panzer regiments in early 1944, this vehicle saw most use on the Western Front, notably in Normandy with the 12th SS Division.

GERMANY

JAGDPANZER 38(T) HETZER

The Hetzer was a small but powerful vehicle based on the chassis of the Panzer 38(t) light tank. It was the smallest fully armoured vehicle to mount the 75mm (2.95in) PaK 39 anti-tank gun and was particularly useful in urban fighting.

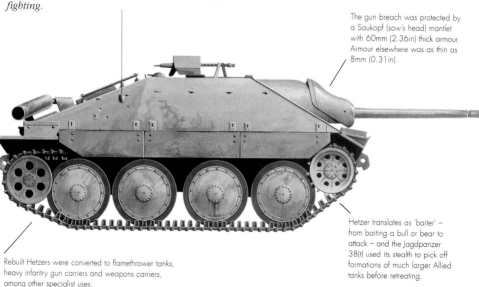

The gun breach was protected by a Saukopf (sow's head) mantlet with 60mm (2.36in) thick armour. Armour elsewhere was as thin as 8mm (0.31in).

Hetzer translates as 'baiter' – from baiting a bull or bear to attack – and the Jagdpanzer 38(t) used its stealth to pick off formations of much larger Allied tanks before retreating.

Rebuilt Hetzers were converted to flamethrower tanks, heavy infantry gun carriers and weapons carriers, among other specialist uses.

The gun had limited traverse (5 degrees to the left and 11 to the right) and elevation (12 degrees up, 6 degrees down).

Secondary armament was limited to a single machine gun, which was mounted on the roof and controlled remotely from inside.

Armour was light with a maximum of 60mm (2.36in) thickness, but this was made up for by the difficulty in seeing and hitting the diminutive vehicle.

The Hetzer was very cramped for the four-man crew, a situation slightly relieved on 100 vehicles that had no recoil mechanism for the main gun, the recoil being absorbed by the vehicle itself.

GERMANY

103

GERMANY

A compact design, little taller than a man, the SdKfz 138/2 Hetzer was an effective tank hunter design and was a better use of resources than most of the larger German Jagdpanzer vehicles. When

The Hetzer was a useful, fast and effective little tank destroyer.

the Germans took over the Czech Skoda and Praga tank factories, they concentrated initially on producing the Czech-designed Panzer 38(t), but by 1943 this design was obsolete. General Guderian, at that time Inspector of Armoured Units, called for a light tank destroyer with a low silhouette to replace the existing towed and light self-propelled anti-tank guns, and the Panzer 38(t) was a suitable basis for a new vehicle.

After trials in December 1943, production commenced in April 1944 and the first tank-

Jagdpanzer 38(t) Hetzer

Powerplant:	119kW (160hp) Praga AC2 inline six-cylinder petrol engine
Performance:	The Hetzer had a maximum road speed of 39km/h (24mph) and a road range of 250km (155 miles)
Dimensions:	length: 6.2m (20ft 4in); width: 2.5m (8ft 2in); height: 2.1m (6ft 11in)

An American GI examines the compact size of the Hetzer light tank destroyer.

hunter battalions were equipped in July 1944. Its 75mm (2.95in) gun was effective against the armour of most of its opponents, and front-line reports were very favourable. Accordingly, production was stepped up, aiming for a rate of 1000 per month, and deliveries ceased only when the factories were overrun in May 1945. After the war, production was resumed for the Czech army and 160 were exported to Switzerland, serving until the 1970s.

GERMANY

FLAKPANZER IV WIRBELWIND

*To provide anti-aircraft defence for panzer
battalions, the Wirbelwind AA tank was created
by converting obsolete Panzer IVs by mounting
the widely used Flak 38 20mm AA gun in a new
turret. It was not a great success.*

The Wirbelwind did not appear
on the battlefront until after the
Normandy invasion, when it
might have been most useful.
Only 87 were converted.

The 20mm (0.78in)
Flak 38 four-barrelled
cannon could be
elevated to a vertical
position or depressed
to −10 degrees.

Panzer IVs withdrawn from the Eastern Front
for overhaul formed the basis of the
Wirbelwind and the Ostwind.

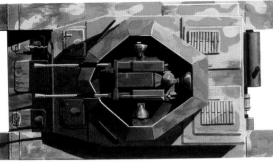

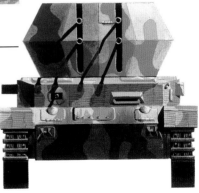

The armour on the new turret was only 10mm (0.39in) thick, providing little protection for the gun crew.

The Wirbelwind was replaced by the Ostwind, which had the same type of octagonal turret but mounted a single-barrelled 37mm (1.46in) Flak 43 cannon.

The Wirbelwind was a simple conversion of the Panzer IV tank, mounting an octagonal turret on the turret ring. The turret was rotated by hand.

GERMANY

107

GERMANY

The Wirbelwind (whirlwind) was the German answer to the increasing threat posed to German armoured columns by the Allied fighter-bombers. Most earlier self-propelled anti-aircraft mounts had single or twin 20mm (0.78in) armament and little armour protection for the crew.

The Flakpanzer IV was designed to correct both these deficiencies by having a four-barrelled 20mm (0.78in) weapon in a fully enclosed open-topped turret. The turret was based on the proven Panzer IV Ausf J chassis, which allowed it to be integrated into the anti-aircraft platoons of the panzer regiments with little difficulty. The Wirbelwind retained the bow-mounted machine gun of the Panzer IV and, with the main gun unit able to depress to –10 degree elevation, it also had a certain anti-personnel capability.

The crew of a camouflaged Wirbelwind awaits the next wave of Allied fighter-bombers.

Wirbelwinds were themselves vulnerable to air attack, and many were knocked out by Allied aircraft.

Flakpanzer IV Wirbelwind

Powerplant:	228kW (300hp) Maybach HL120TRM V-12 petrol engine
Performance:	The Wirbelwind had a maximum road speed of 38km/h (24mph) and a road range of 200km (125 miles)
Dimensions:	length: 5.92m (19ft); width: 2.9m (9ft 6in); height: 2.76m (9ft 1in)

All of these vehicles were conversions, rather than new-builds, and only 86 were produced, beginning in July 1944. Two inherent problems with the design were the thin (16mm/0.62in) armour plate on the turret and the hand-traversed turret mechanism, which proved difficult to operate in combat.

By the autumn of 1944, the 20mm (0.78in) Flak 38 was found to be much less effective than the 37mm (1.45in) Flak 43 and production of Wirbelwinds was halted in favour of the Ostwind (east wind), a very similar vehicle with the single-barrel 37mm (1.45in) gun.

GERMANY

STURMMÖRSER TIGER

The Sturmmörser Tiger was created by converting the Tiger E battle tank to fire huge rocket-assisted projectiles in the assault role. Very few were actually built.

Only 12 projectiles could be stowed inside, but others could be lifted off a supply vehicle with the built-in hand-operated crane system mounted at the rear of the superstructure and lowered through a large roof hatch.

The weight of the Sturmtiger was 65 tonnes (66 tons) compared to the 57 tonnes (57.9 tons) of a standard Tiger.

A crew of seven operated the Sturmtiger in action, although most travelled in other vehicles between firing points.

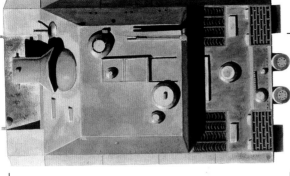

Handling the shells, which weighed 345kg (761lb) each, was a delicate and dangerous business and another winch system was installed inside to move the shells from their racks to the breech of the projector.

The main weapon of the Sturmtiger was the 380mm (14.9in) StuM RW61 rocket mortar. An MG 34 machine gun was provided for self-defence.

The ball-mounted raketenwerfer (rocket projector) was mounted slightly off-centre and had a series of holes around its rim for venting rocket gases.

GERMANY

111

GERMANY

The Sturmmörser Tiger, or Sturmtiger, was an extraordinary conversion of the Tiger I tank to fire a heavy rocket-assisted projectile against fixed targets. It could operate in the direct assault role or provide indirect fire at ranges of up to 6km (3.7 miles).

The 380mm (14.9in) mortar itself was originally a naval design intended for use by

U-boats against land targets, and could be seen as an ancestor of the ballistic missiles on today's submarines. When the Kriegsmarine dropped the idea, it was taken up as a land-based weapon, and the only suitable carriage for it was the Tiger tank.

In 1943, troops on the Eastern Front had requested such a weapon (of perhaps 210mm/8.2in) to engage difficult targets with indirect fire and also to keep up with a mobile front line. The Sturmtiger promised this and more, but by the time production was underway in August 1944, Germany was on the defensive and only a small number were ordered.

Alkett made the conversion using Tiger Ausf Es as the basis, upon which was added a new box-like superstructure with a sloped front. An integral crane was needed to lift the

A close-up of the unique, short-barrelled rocket projector of the Sturmmörser Tiger.

Sturmmörser Tiger

Powerplant:	522kW (700hp) Maybach HL210P45 V-12 petrol engine
Performance:	The Sturmtiger had a road speed of 40km/h (25mph) and a road range of 120km (75 miles)
Dimensions:	length: 6.28m (20ft 7in); width: 3.57m (11ft 4in); height: 2.85m (9ft 4in)

The Sturmmörser was ineffective in the defensive role and most were destroyed or captured in early 1945.

heavy shells and load them aboard the vehicle through a hatch in the roof. Estimates for the number produced vary between 10 and 81, but a likely figure is 18. They were issued to three different Sturmmörser companies and their giant mortars played a role in the defence of Germany rather than being used for their intended purpose of blowing apart enemy strongpoints with a single shot.

GERMANY

JAGDPANZER VI JAGDTIGER

Apart from the abortive Maus super heavy tank, the Jagdtiger was the ultimate expression of Hitler's obsession with larger and larger AFVs. The Jagdtiger was an impressive but ultimately tactically ineffective vehicle.

Tank destroyers typically had a fixed superstructure with a limited traverse gun. The Jagdtiger's gun could be elevated to 15 degrees and moved 10 degrees to each side.

Armour ranged from 40mm (1.5in) thickness on the superstructure top and upper hull to 250mm (9.8in) thickness on the front of the superstructure.

Only 77 Jagdtigers were ever delivered due to disruption caused by bombing, which also affected gun production.

A small number of Jagdtigers were built with Porsche-designed suspension, but the majority had the same Henschel suspension as on the King Tiger.

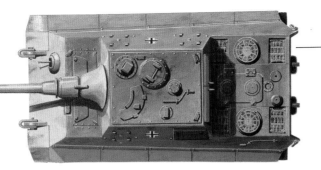

The crew of six included two gun loaders, who were needed to handle the 128mm (5in) shells, which weighed 26.4kg (58lb, 4oz) each.

It is thought that some Jagdtigers were delivered with relatively puny 88mm (3.46in) guns due to a shortage of the 128mm (5in) PaK 44 L/55.

An MG 34 machine gun was fitted in a ball mount on the glacis plate and an MG 42 machine gun was carried inside for crew protection.

The Jagdtiger (hunting tiger) was the heaviest AFV to serve in World War II and carried the second-largest gun of any wartime tank or tank destroyer. Designed as an anti-tank gun, the 128mm (5in) gun could theoretically defeat 148mm (5.8in) armour at 2000m (6560ft), which meant, in effect, any tank in the world. The Jagdtiger's own upper frontal armour was a

This basically intact Jagdtiger was captured in April 1945 by US forces.

record 250mm (9.8in), impenetrable by anything short of a battleship. It was developed, as was the practice of the time, as the tank destroyer counterpart to the latest battle tank, the Tiger II. The design received Hitler's approval in October 1943

The Jagdtiger was hugely powerful but very cumbersome.

Jagdpanzer VI Jagdtiger

Powerplant:	522kW (700hp) Maybach HL230P30 V-12 petrol engine
Performance:	The Jagdtiger had a maximum road speed of 38km/h (24mph) and a road range of 170km (105 miles)
Dimensions:	length: 10.65m (34ft 11in); width: 3.63m (11ft 1in); height: 2.95m (9ft 8in)

and a prototype was ready in April 1944. Orders were that, after 150 were completed, production was to be halted in favour of Panthers, but this was reversed and production restarted in January 1945.

The two units that received Jagdtigers, one Panzerjäger battalion and one independent heavy tank battalion, fought on the Western Front, the former in the Ardennes offensive of December 1944, and the latter in defence of Germany, including at the Remagen Bridge in March 1945. With the same powerplant as much smaller tanks, the heavy Jagdtiger was fuel-thirsty, slow and hard to conceal. Eventually most were overwhelmed by infantry with bazookas or charges that struck at the most vulnerable parts – the wheels and tracks – and they became mileposts on the road to Berlin.

GERMANY

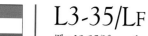

L3-35/Lᴘ

The L3-35/Lf was the flamethrower version of the CV L35 tankette. About 2000 light tanks on the same chassis were built between 1933 and 1943.

The CV 33 tanks and their flamethower derivatives had no turrets as such, but a raised superstructure mounting the main armament, usually machine guns but on the L3-35/Lf a flame projector.

The CV 33 series of light tanks were exported to countries including Afghanistan, Albania, Bolivia, Brazil, China and Nationalist Spain in the 1930s.

With the Italian armistice in 1943, the Germans took over the survivors and issued them mostly to police and labour camp units.

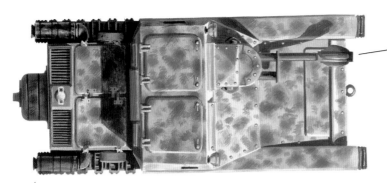

The Lf in L3-35/Lf stood for 'lanciafiamme', or flamethrower. The vehicle usually towed a 500kg (1102lb) trailer containing the fuel for the flame projector.

One interesting feature of the CV 33 was its air-portability. The tank (or, more correctly, tankette) could be slung under a transport aircraft, an idea later taken up by the Americans for use by airborne forces.

The CV tankettes were tiny vehicles. The L3-35/Lf was only 1.3m (4ft 3in) tall and had a crew of two.

The hull was of riveted and bolted construction, as were the majority of Italian tanks, the armour plate being only 5.15mm (0.2in) thick.

ITALY

ITALY

Italy specialized in light tanks with a few designs in the medium category. Those light tanks designed pre-war were close relatives of a British Carden-Lloyd tankette design, examples of which had been purchased in 1929. The Italians named their versions Carro Veloce (fast tank) and the most important, the CV 33, was designed in

The tiny L3-35/Lf flame-thrower tank towed its flame fuel supply in a trailer.

1933 and entered service two years later. Over 1300 were produced by Fiat-Ansaldo in the first order alone, some for export. These simple vehicles had no turret as such, a rear-mounted petrol engine and front-wheel drive, and one or two light machine guns as the main armament. Twin machine gun versions were unofficially known as CV 35s, and the final production version was the CV L38, some of which were rebuilt with a 20mm (0.78in) cannon.

The ability of the CV tanks to tow an ammunition trailer (having evolved from what was essentially a light weapons tractor) meant that it was also used in a flame-thrower version. The jellied petroleum

L3-35/Lf

Powerplant:	41kW (60hp) Hispano-Suiza 12Y-31 12-cylinder V-type
Performance:	The L3-35/Lf had a maximum road speed of 42km/h (26mph)
Dimensions:	length: 3.2m (10ft 5in); width: 1.42m (4ft 8in); height: 1.3m (4ft 3in)

(napalm) was kept in a 500kg (1102lb) trailer and piped forward to the flame projector, which was mounted in the centre of the superstructure face. This idea was used later by the British in the Normandy landings. Called a 'carro d'assalto lancia-fiamme' (flamethrower assault tank), it was initially designated the L35/Lf and later the L3-35/Lf.

The L/35Lf was effective against troops armed with light weapons.

ITALY

121

Carro Armato M11/39

The M11/39 was Italy's first medium tank. Built only in small numbers, its riveted armour, limited traverse gun and crew layout were all obsolete by the outbreak of war. Good features included an effective gun (for its calibre) and diesel engine.

Armour plate joined by rivets was widely used on pre-war tanks, but in combat the rivets would ricochet around the interior if the tank was hit.

The main gun was a 37mm (1.45in) Vickers-Terni L/40 cannon, which was a reasonable weapon for its day against light armour.

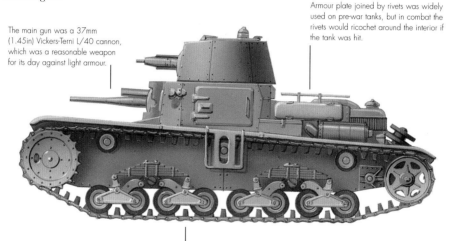

The suspension comprised double-wheeled articulated bogies, mounted on leaf springs, a rather antiquated system for a wartime tank.

CARRO ARMATO M11/39

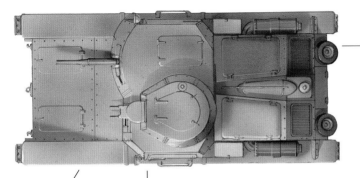

The upper rear part of the hull formed a stowage box for tools and crew equipment.

The top turret was fully rotatable by hand and contained an 8mm (0.31in) Breda machine gun.

The sponson arrangement for the main gun allowed a traverse of only 30 degrees laterally.

The M11/39 had a crew of three. The gunner loaded, aimed and fired the main weapon.

Vision for the driver was provided by a simple slit within a hinged plate in front of his compartment.

ITALY

123

Combat experience in Spain revealed the inadequacies of Italy's two-man CV 33, and light tanks in general. Using a 1935 8 tonne (7.8 ton) tank as a basis, a new medium tank was developed in 1937, but not until 1939 were 100 ordered.

The cramped M11/39 had very light armament and armour.

The Carro Armato (literally: armoured car) M11/39 shared with the US M3 Lee the principle of having its main armament, a

37mm (1.46in) cannon in a hull sponson and secondary armament in a rotating turret. Early examples had six road wheels, but most had eight. The design also retained riveted armour, one of the weaknesses of the CV 33 and other Italian tanks.

Seventy M11/39s first saw action at Sidi Azeis, Libya, in August 1940. The slab-sided armour, no more than 30mm (1.1in) thick, but mainly 14mm (0.5in), was inadequate against British Matilda and Valentine tanks, let alone 25pdr anti-tank guns. Though the diesel engine was resistant to fire, large numbers were soon knocked out in combat.

Five M11/39s were captured by the 6th Australian Division and used against the Italians at Tobruk in January 1941. Soon afterwards the type was withdrawn from the battlefield in favour of the improved M13/40, which shared many components.

British tanks and guns destroyed with ease many M11/39s in North Africa.

Carro Armato M11/39

Powerplant:	78kW (105hp) SPA 8T eight-cylinder diesel engine
Performance:	The M11/39 had a maximum road speed of 33km/h (21mph) and a road range of 200km (125 miles)
Dimensions:	length: 4.73m (15ft 6in); width: 2.18m (7ft 2in); height: 2.30m (7ft 7in)

ITALY

125

CARRO ARMATO L6/40

The Italian L6/40 light tank saw action in North Africa, Italy and in Russia and was effective in the reconnaissance role. Against enemy armour, however, it was hopelessly outclassed.

Armour was mainly riveted and bolted steel plate. Thickness ranged from 6mm to 30mm (0.2–1.18in) on the hull front.

The torsion bar suspension had double-wheel bogies and trailing suspension arms.

The chassis was built on that of the private venture Fiat Ansaldo 5 tonne (4.9 ton) light tank, but with a strengthened suspension and with longer ground contact.

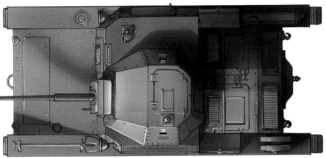

As was common with these mini tanks, the turrret was offset to one side and the driver sat in the hull alongside it.

Like most Italian tanks, the L6/40 had a prominent boarding step on the track guards.

The L6/40 had prominent headlights on the superstructure. Although a useful driving aid, they were easily damaged in battle.

The L6/40 had a crew of only two, a driver and a commander-gunner who fired both the 20mm (0.78in) cannon and the coaxial machine gun.

ITALY

127

ITALY

The L6/40's commander also had to load and fire the 20mm (0.78in) gun.

Designed to replace the L3 (CV 33) light tank, the Fiat L6/40 had as its basis a Fiat-Ansaldo tracked chassis originally intended for export. In 1936, two armed prototypes were delivered for testing. They had either two 8mm (0.31in) machine guns or one 37mm (1.46in) cannon in the turret plus a sponson-mounted machine gun. The production vehicles had a 20mm (0.78in) Breda cannon and one machine gun.

A great improvement on the CV 33, the Italian army ordered 283 L6/40s, most of which were delivered in 1941 and 1942, although the order was later reduced. Due to the long delay between invention and deployment, the L6/40 was obsolete by the time it first saw action.

Lacking in medium and heavy tanks, the Italians were forced to use light tanks where they were unsuited. When faced with British or Russian tanks or anti-tank guns, the L6/40 was unable to defend itself.

Nonetheless, the L6/40 was a reasonable vehicle, equivalent to the German Panzer II. They saw action in North Africa, Italy and in the Soviet Union.

Variants included a version in which the 20mm (0.78in) cannon was replaced by a flamethrower with a tank containing 200 litres (44 gallons) of flame liquid. A command version had an open roof and extra radios.

Carro Armato L6/40

Powerplant:	52kW (70hp) SPA 18 D 8 4-cylinder petrol engine
Performance:	The L6/40 had a maximum road speed of 42km/h (26 mph) and a road range of 200km (125 miles)
Dimensions:	length: 3.78m (12ft 5in); width: 1.92m (6ft 4in); height: 2.03m (6ft 8in)

The L6/40 was used as the basis of the Semovente L40 47/32 self-propelled gun. This had the turret removed and replaced by a 47mm (1.85in) gun with 49 rounds. A few L6/40s saw service with the Italian army as late as 1952.

The L6/40 was a good light tank, but was used where medium tanks would have been needed.

ITALY

CARRO ARMATO M15/42

*The M15/42 was the final development of the
medium tank series begun with the M11/39.
By the time it appeared in 1942, its armour
and armament were obsolescent. Despite its
faults, it was the best Italian tank of the war
to be produced in any quantity.*

The M15/42 had a crew of
four: commander, driver, machine
gunner and loader.

The Germans used
considerable numbers
as the PzKpfw
M15/42 738(i).

The turret had powered traverse
for the first time on an Italian
medium tank. The gun was a
high-velocity long-barrelled Model
47/40 47mm (1.85in) gun.

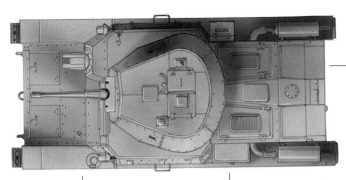

Unlike its predecessors the M15/42 had a petrol engine. This was more prone to fire, but simplified logistics.

The M15/42 usually had four machine guns, two of which were in a dual mount in the hull. Another was coaxial with the main gun and the fourth could be fitted on an anti-aircraft mount.

There were extra stowage points for water cans on the M15/42, but these were not always used.

The earlier M13/40 and M14/41 had a large entrance hatch on the left side of the upper hull. The M15/52 relocated this to the other side.

ITALY

131

ITALY

Poor performance of the Carro Armato M11/39 in Libya made a replacement a necessity. The M13/40 was the result, with a new turret and powerful 47mm (1.85in) gun. The sponson was relegated to machine guns, usually a paired arrangement of Model 1938 8mm (0.31in) weapons, and a loader joined the crew. The type first saw action in North Africa in December 1940, serving later in Italy, Greece and Yugoslavia. Its thicker armour was mainly bolted around a steel frame, but often cracked when hit. Many were captured and then used by British and Australian units.

Although the most advanced Italian tank of the war, few M15/42s saw combat.

The M13/40 was further developed into the M14/41 and the definitive M15/42, with its long-barrelled 47mm (1.85in) gun, heavily

A column of M13/40s advance across the Libyan desert. The M15/42 was a development of the M13/40 with a better gun and equipment.

Carro Armato M15/42

Powerplant:	108kW (145hp) SPA 8-TM-41 V-8 petrol engine
Performance:	The M15/42 had a maximum road speed of 35km/h (22mph) and a road range of 200km (125 miles)
Dimensions:	length: 4.92m (16ft 2in); width: 2.2m (7ft 3in); height: 2.38m (7ft 10in)

armoured mantlet, more powerful petrol engine, better sand filters, and more external stowage. Only 82 M15/42s were built, compared to 2000 of the M13/40 and M14/41 combined. From March 1943, the chassis were used for self-propelled guns.

Most M15/42s went to the Ariete Division, which was deployed to stop the Germans entering Rome. Some were captured and then used by the Germans.

ITALY

133

SEMOVENTE DA 75/18

The DA 75, also known as the M41 self-propelled gun, was intended as a counter to the Soviet T-34, but was never in fact sent to the Eastern Front. Most were used in Sicily against US and British forces.

The crew entered the fixed turret via hinged doors. Simple fixed steps aided boarding.

The DA 75 was a low profile vehicle with a very flat roof. There were few fittings for attaching ancilliary equipment, such as tools or crew bedding.

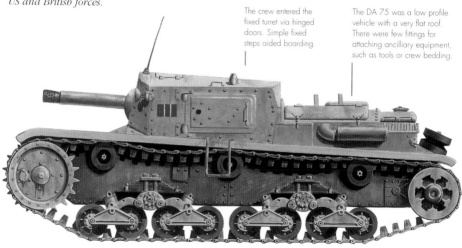

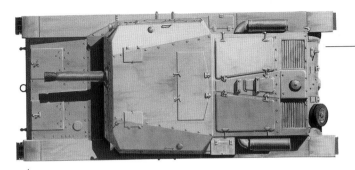

The Semoventes dispensed with the high turret and the superstructure of the M15/42 and replaced them with a box-like fixed riveted structure with no commander's cupola. Turret access was through a large hinged hatch cover, which opened to the rear.

The improved M43 105/25 was completed in smaller numbers, but sported a much more effective 105mm (4.1in) gun. It likewise saw most service with the German Army.

The gun was offset slightly to make room for the driver/gunner, who had only an armoured slit for vision.

In German service, the Semovente was renamed Sturmgeschütz M42 mit 75/18 850(i), or StuG M42. Including vehicles built by the Germans, 294 were issued to Wehrmacht divisions in Italy and the Balkans in 1943 and 1944. By the end of 1944, 200 had been destroyed, captured or abandoned.

ITALY

135

ITALY

The Italian army relied heavily on German armoured support and built mainly light tanks during the war. For the Italians, the war was not going well, and most tank production therefore ceased in favour of self-propelled guns that could be pressed into service as tank destroyers.

This Semovente is armed with the original 75/18 gun.

The principal example of this was the Semovente M42 series mounting a variety of guns, mainly of 75mm (2.95in) calibre. The basis for these vehicles was the Carro

136

Armato M15/42 tank built by Fait-Ansaldo from 1942 onwards.

Some 200 vehicles with the short 75/18 (75mm, 18 calibres) gun were ordered in March 1943 and an order for another 500 with a 75/34 gun soon followed. Trouble with the mounting of the 75/34 prevented its earlier introduction. A machine gun was stowed inside and could be mounted on the forward lip of the hatch for anti-aircraft defence, leaving the gunner rather exposed. The engine was a V-8 petrol unit. Early

Semovente DA 75/18

Powerplant:	108kW (145hp) SPA 15-TM-41 V-8 petrol engine
Performance:	The DA 75/18 had a maximum road speed of 38km/h (24mph) and a road range of 230km (143 miles)
Dimensions:	length: 5.04m (16ft 6in); width 2.23m (7ft 4in); height: 1.85m (6ft 1in)

versions of the M15/42 tank had a lower powered, but also lower maintenance, diesel unit. However, diesel supplies to the Italian front became increasingly unreliable and petrol engines were substituted. In September 1943, the Germans took control of the factory.

The Semovente was Italy's equivalent of the German StuG.

ITALY

TYPE 95 KYUGO

*The Type 95 may have been the best Japanese
light tank to be built in large numbers, but it
contained faults that would have been
unacceptable on any Western tank. It was
known both as the Ha-Go and the Kyugo.*

The main gun was a Type
94 37mm (1.45in)
cannon. The commander
doubled as the loader and
gunner for this weapon.

The rear-facing Type 91 6.5mm
(0.25in) machine gun was fired by
the commander/gunner. Because of
its position, it had an even poorer
field of fire than the main gun.

The suspension was found to be unstable in pitch during cross-
country operations, so vehicles were modified so that the bogies
were connected by an inverted triangular-shaped brace.

The one-man turret of the Type 95 did not fully rotate, being limited to a 45-degree forward arc.

The Type 95's six-cylinder diesel engine gave a high power-to-weight ratio and good acceleration, and was air-cooled using turbo impellers.

The three-man crew included a bow machine-gunner, who also acted as general mechanic.

JAPAN

The Japanese made no effective tanks and failed to employ those they did have in sufficient quantities. The most common tank was the Type 95, known to the manufacturer as the Ha-Go and the Army as the Kyugo. Accepted in 1935 (hence its

Japanese infantry hitch a ride on a Type 95 Ha-Go.

designation, a reference to the 95th year of the current Imperial era), this tank was one of the oldest designs of the war – and seriously flawed. It was based on the Type 94 tankette, whose armour of 4–12mm (0.15–0.47in) was vulnerable even to rifle fire. The minimum 6mm (0.23in) on the Type 95 could be defeated by light weapons, in one case a 0.303in bullet strike. M4 Shermans frequently blew holes right through them. The Type 95 had intakes vulnerable to petrol bombs, and the turret could be jammed with a knife blade. The

Type 95 Kyugo

Powerplant:	89.5kW (120hp) Mitsubishi NVD six-cylinder inline diesel
Performance:	The Type 95 had a maximum road speed of 46km/h (28mph) and a road range of 160km (100 miles)
Dimensions:	Length: 4.38m (14ft 4in); width: 2.05m (6ft 9in); height: 2.18m (7ft 2in)

one-man turret had a total traverse of only 45 degrees. The rear-facing machine gun was meant to cover the aft hemisphere, but even then there were large gaps in the field of fire. Vision was very poor despite numerous open vision slits, which increased crew vulnerability, not being made of glass block.

An armour-piercing shell knocked out this Type 95.

JAPAN

141

JAPAN

TYPE 97 CHI-HA

The Type 97 Medium Chi-Ha was as good as any contemporary light tanks, but remained in production long after it had been surpassed by Allied designs.

The Chi-Ha's main armament was a 47mm (1.85in) Type 97 cannon, backed up by two 7.7mm (0.3in) Type 97 machine guns, one in the bow and one in the rear of the turret.

The Chi-Ha was mainly used in the infantry support role and was supplied with high explosive (HE) shells. These were largely useless against heavier Allied tanks.

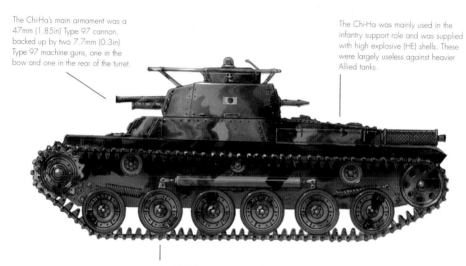

The Chi-Ha's suspension was refined compared to previous Japanese tanks, but still gave the crew an uncomfortable ride over uneven terrain.

There was capacity for 100 rounds of 57mm (2.24in) ammunition in the vehicle and 2475 rounds of machine gun ammunition.

The Type 97 had a two-man turret, which at least allowed the rear-facing machine gun to be manned while the commander directed his attentions elsewhere.

The thickest armour was on the vertical parts of the turret and was 33mm (1.2in) steel. Elsewhere, the armour was mainly 25mm (0.9in) thickness.

JAPAN

143

JAPAN

A medium tank by Japanese standards, the Type 97, or Chi-Ha, was the replacement for the obsolescent Type 89. The Chi-Ha was evaluated alongside the three-man Type 97 Chi-Ni designed by the Army General Staff, and after some

An Allied soldier tries out a captured Chi-Ha for size.

debate over the virtues of lighter, cheaper tanks versus heavier, costlier ones, the larger four-man Chi-Ha was chosen for production.

The Shinhoto Chi-Ha had a new turret and larger 47mm (1.85in) gun.

Type 97 Chi-Ha

Powerplant:	127kW (170hp) Mitsubishi Type 97 V-12 diesel engine
Performance:	The Type 97 had a maximum road speed of 39km/h (24mph) and a road range of 240km (149 miles)
Dimensions:	length: 5.5m (18ft); width: 2.33m (7ft 8in); height: 2.23m (7ft 4in)

Between 1937 and 1940, about 300 were built, mainly by Mitsubishi. The Chi-Ha was essentially a scaled-up light tank Type 95 with a two-man turret offset to the right side of the vehicle. The driver and bow machine gunner sat in the forward hull and at the rear was the engine, which was diesel-powered, the best choice for AFV engines. A successful development was the Shinhoto ('modified turret') Chi-Ha, which had the turret of the Type 1 medium tank and a 47mm (1.85in) high-velocity gun. This more effective version was produced until the war's end, along with specialist versions, such as bridgelayers, mine flail tanks and command tanks. The command version, the Shi-Ki, had extra radio equipment in place of armament and a dummy gun to avoid this being singled out by enemy gunners.

JAPAN

145

M3A1 Stuart III

The Stuart was the standard US and British light tank of the early war years. It was extremely well liked by its crews for its reliability and was said to be a 'real honey', hence its nickname. This example served with the British 7th Armoured Division.

The M3's lack of range was partly remedied by adding auxiliary fuel tanks on later models.

The official British name for the M3 was General Stuart, usually abbreviated to Stuart. M3s were also known unofficially as 'Honeys'.

The standard engine was a seven-cylinder Continental petrol unit, but many of the early M3s were supplied with a nine-cylinder Guiberson diesel without change of designation.

Initial versions had a riveted turret as well as hull armour, but this was soon replaced by a cast armour turret because of the tendency of rivets to 'pop' when the tank was hit.

The M3's 37mm (1.45in) cannon was inadequate against German tanks, although it was usually effective against Japanese armour.

The initial M3 version had a pair of machine guns in the sponsons for operation by the driver, but these were often removed. Their mounts can be seen here.

The original M3, and the later welded-hull M3A1 and M3A3 versions were soon outclassed in tank-versus-tank combat, but proved useful in reconnaissance units and in theatres such as China and Burma, where their small size was an asset on rough jungle trails.

UNITED STATES

A Stuart III crewman mans the anti-aircraft gun, Germany, 1945.

Developed from a series of light tanks (initially called 'combat cars') produced in the 1930s, the M3 was the main tank type in service with the US Army at the outbreak of war. Compared to its predecessors, the M3 had increased armour (especially on frontal areas), a stronger suspension with larger trailing idler wheel and no vision ports in the turret. Most of these improvements came about in light of combat reports from Europe in 1939–40. The M3 was approved for production in July 1940 and this began in March 1941, when previous contracts had been completed. M3s were sent to Britain under Lend-Lease as soon as they became available and were available in strength for battles in the Western desert by November 1941. They proved a useful addition to British tank strength throughout the desert war, although they were short on range.

Early M3s were supplied with either petrol or diesel engines. This caused logistic

M3A1 Stuart III

Powerplant:	185.5kW (250hp) Continental W-670 seven-cylinder radial petrol engine
Performance:	The M3A1 had a maximum road speed of 58km/h (36mph) and a road range of 113km (70 miles)
Dimensions:	length: 4.54m (14ft 10in); width: 2.22m (7ft 4in); height: 2.3m (7ft 7in)

problems, especially for the British, who named the diesel versions Stuart IIs. The US Army declared the M3 series obsolete in July 1943, having introduced the larger M5, but the British and other users continued operating Stuarts until the end of the war, and well after in some cases.

The British-produced Stuart I had a petrol engine.

M3 LEE

The M3 Medium was America's first worthy main battle tank. It first saw combat with British forces as the Grant Mk I and a modified version became the Lee (after General Grant's opponent in the American Civil War). It was important to both US and British forces in the early war years.

The turret contained a 37mm (1.45in) M5 cannon and the cupola had a 7.62mm (0.3in) machine gun. The turret gun was fully rotatable by hand, a 360 degree sweep taking 20 seconds.

The main gun of the Lee/Grant was a 75mm (2.95in) M2 with only 30 degrees of traverse. One coaxial and two hull machine guns were fitted on some models.

T24203

The running gear of the M3 Lee/Grant became the basis for many other vehicles, including (in modified form) the M4 Sherman series.

This is an early production M3 with a riveted hull and large side doors. Later models featured cast hulls, gyro-stabilization for the guns and power traverse for the turret.

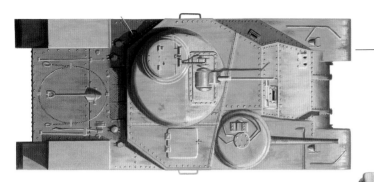

Australian forces used M3s in the Pacific jungles, where their high profile and unusual gun configuration proved very useful.

The main gun was a development of a World War I French weapon and was appreciated for its dual-purpose capability, able to fire armour-piercing (AP) rounds against tanks and high explosive (HE) shot in an infantry support role.

The suspension inherited from the M2 turned out to be inadequate for the heavier M3 and was redesigned with heavier springs.

151

In 1940, the largest gun on an American tank had a calibre of 37mm (1.46in). At the same time, German tanks with 75mm (2.95in) guns were cutting a swathe through the armoured units of Great Britain and France – which relied on 37mm (1.46in) gun tanks. The US Army's Chief of Infantry demanded that US medium tanks carry 75mms (2.95in), but the only suitable

The M3 Lee was larger and heavier than any previous US tank.

vehicle was the M2A1. This carried eight machine guns in its superstructure, but could not mount such a gun in its small turret. The solution was to mount the 75mm (2.95in) gun in the right side of the hull. The result was the M3 medium tank, which was developed and put into production with remarkable haste.

By August 1941, production had begun at three plants, one of which had been purpose-built. A further two plants produced M3s to an initial British order of 500. Named Grant Is (after US General Ulysses S. Grant), these had a contoured cast turret with no

A crewman cleans out the main gun of an M3 in Tunisia in 1943.

M3 Lee

Powerplant:	253.5kW (340hp) Continental, R-975-EC2 or E1 radial petrol engine
Performance:	The M3 had a maximum road speed of 42km/h (27mph) and a road range of 193km (120 miles)
Dimensions:	length: 5.63m (18ft 6in); width: 8ft 11in (2.7m); height: 3.12m (10ft 3in)

cupola. The first British tanks able to outgun the German panzers, they were of critical importance at the Battle of Gazala in May 1942. The configuration of the tank, which needed to be turned towards the target to engage it with the main gun, was a disadvantage, as was the high profile and the riveted, welded armour. In December 1942, the last of 6258 vehicles was delivered, and by April 1944 it was declared obsolete.

UNITED STATES

M4A2 SHERMAN III

*Built in huge numbers and many variants, the
M4 Sherman was not without its faults, such as
low-powered guns and a propensity to catch
fire, but it was the most important tank in the
US arsenal throughout World War II.*

The M4A2 had a five-man crew:
a commander in the turret right
rear, a gunner in turret right front,
a loader in turret left rear, a driver
in hull left front and an assistant
driver in hull right front.

DORIS

53

US armament differences were explicit, and the suffix HVSS indicated
horizontal volume spring suspension. Introduced in mid-1944, this let individual
wheels be changed. Those AFVs that were retained post-war had HVSS.

Although the US later introduced diesel tank
propulsion generally, the majority of
Shermans were petrol-fuelled.

The tendency for the Sherman's internally stowed ammunition to catch fire when the tank was hit brought about the nicknames 'Ronson' and 'Zippo' (after the cigarette lighters) and 'Tommy Cooker' for British M4s.

The introduction of wet stowage for ammunition was an attempt to combat fires. The suffix 'W' was used to indicate this, as in M4A3(75)W. One-hundred-and-forty-three litres (31 gallons) of water mixed with antifreeze and an anti-corrosion product called 'ammudamp' were needed for 100 shells.

In combat, 25mm (0.98in) appliqué armour was added on the side of the upper hull to protect the ammunition stowage. To defeat German hollow-charge weapons such as the Panzerfaust, spare track pieces were welded onto hulls and turrets or sandbags were affixed, sometimes with quite elaborate wooden frames.

UNITED STATES

The M3 Medium was always regarded as an interim solution to US tank needs until a turret could be produced to mount a 75mm (2.95in) gun. Improvements in casting technology and success with the 37mm (1.46in) turret on the M3 encouraged development of a

A pair of Shermans provide support for US troops in the Philippines in 1945.

compact, curved unit, plans for which were drawn up by March 1941.

The Armored Force Board was offered five options based on this turret and selected the simplest, which involved fitting it to a modified M3 hull and chassis. The T6 Medium mock-up was approved in May, and the pilot model delivered to the Aberdeen Proving Ground, Maryland, in September 1941.

One change was the elimination of a machine gun cupola. The hull was of welded construction, following the practice of later M3s, and had a prominent side hatch, which was deleted for production. The T6 was standardized as the M4 Medium in October 1941. Schedules called for 1000 deliveries per month during 1942, at no fewer than 11 car and locomotive plants and engineering works. A second government tank arsenal, run by Fisher, was built at Grand Blanc, Michigan, in 1942.

The initial production models utilized a Wright radial engine, but the aircraft industry had greater demand for these and for the

The Sherman's gun could be adapted for use as a flamethrower.

M4A2 Sherman III

Powerplant:	280kW (375hp) General Motors 6046 12-cylinder twin inline diesel engine
Performance:	The M4A2 had a maximum road speed of 48km/h (30mph) and a road range of 240km (150 miles)
Dimensions:	length: 5.92m (19ft 5in); height: 2.74m (9ft); width: 2.62m (8ft 7in)

UNITED STATES

UNITED STATES

production capacity, and alternate powerplants were sought. These included both gasoline and diesel automobile/truck engines.

The M4A1, with its distinctive cast hull, was actually the first model to enter production, with deliveries from January 1942. It had the largest single armour castings produced at that time. Early models

had twin hull machine guns and direct-vision blocks on the hull front, later models having many small improvements. Production ceased in January 1944 with 6281 completed, but many thousands were rebuilt and improved before D-Day.

M4A2 models were powered by a twin inline GMC diesel but were otherwise identical to M4A1s. The Marines were the only US users, but many went to the UK, where they became the Sherman II. The M4A3 was the most produced version, and many of these were supplied to the British (as the Sherman IV) and Soviet forces. M4A4s had welded hulls and the 276kW (370hp) Chrysler Multibank (star layout) engine, giving a greater overall length. Production totalled 7499, all from Detroit.

The M4A3E2 'Jumbo' assault tank was a special limited production model with extra

American tank crews rest in the Ardennes, January 1945.

The Sherman Calliope mounted a large rack of rockets on a standard tank, seen here in Belgium, 1945.

heavy armour for use in Europe. The turret was of a new, heavier design, bringing the total weight to 38 tonnes (37.5 tons). The last production version was the M4A3E8 (76mm/3in) HVSS, sometimes nicknamed the 'Easy Eight'. Production of the Sherman ceased in June 1945.

The Sherman's Combat Debut

In June 1942 Winston Churchill requested for British use 300 of the new M4s then entering production. The British Shermans were the very first produced, but some had been issued to US units before President Roosevelt ordered that they be rushed to North Africa. Supplies of both the M4A1 Sherman II and M4A2 Sherman III arrived in Egypt in September 1942 and were hastily modified for desert fighting before battle was joined at El Alamein on 22 October. Some 50 Shermans were written off and 75 disabled, mainly by mines and shell damage to the suspension parts.

However, they defeated many of the German 88mm (3.46in) guns and Panzer IV 'specials' at long range. Post battle evaluation showed the diesel-engined Mk III had better range, cross-country speed and mechanical reliability, and was much less likely to catch fire than the petrol-engined Sherman II.

UNITED STATES

M22 LOCUST

Designed to provide tank support for airborne (parachute and glider) troops, the M22 Locust was designed to be as small and light as possible. It was used in the airborne role on only one occasion, by British forces in early 1945.

The only method of air transport was to attach it beneath modified C-54 transports with the turret removed and stored inside, thus reducing its tactical utility.

Despite its high speed and low footprint, the Locust suffered from the compromises needed for airborne carriage, namely its small gun and thin armour.

The Locust saw limited US or British service after the war, but a few were supplied to Egypt.

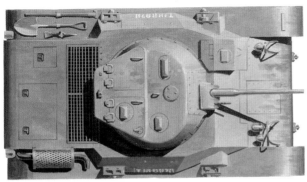

Some Locusts were fitted with a device called a Littlejohn adaptor on the 37mm (1.46in) main gun, which increased barrel length and projectile velocity.

The interior was surprisingly roomy, adequate for a crew of three and with stowage for 50 rounds of 37mm (1.46in) and 2500 rounds of 7.6mm (0.3in) machine gun ammunition.

Four attachments were fitted to allow carriage slung under the C-54.

The M22 was clearly influenced by the M4 Sherman, having mainly cast armour.

UNITED STATES

The M22 was the smallest and lightest American tank of the war and was designed to be air-portable for quick deployment to the battlefield.

The US Army Ordnance Department formulated a requirement for a light tank for the airborne forces in May 1941, with input from the US Armored Force and the US Army Air Force (who would have to transport any such tanks).

The main design features were light weight and compact dimensions to enable carriage in the transport aircraft of the period. Marmon-Herrington submitted the most promising design to meet the specification and their T9 pilot model was delivered in the autumn of 1941.

Despite a main armament of only 37mm (1.46in) calibre and a maximum armour thickness of 25mm (0.9in), the T9 was deemed too heavy, and non-essential fittings, such as power turret traverse and gun gyro-stabilizer, were removed. The revised T9E1 model was accepted and 830 were built, starting in March 1943. It was accepted into US service as the M22 in September 1944, but never saw combat with American forces, partly because there were no gliders large enough to carry it. The M22 was tested as an

The two-man M22 Locust was the smallest American-built tank of World War II.

M22 Locust

Powerplant:	121kW (162hp) Lycoming O-435T six-cylinder radial petrol engine
Performance:	The Locust had a maximum road speed of 64km/h (40mph) and a road range of 217km (135 miles)
Dimensions:	length: 3.93m (12ft 11in); width: 2.16m (7ft 1in); height: 1.82m (6ft 1in)

The M22 was designed to be transported by large gliders such as the British Hamilcar.

underslung load fitted to a C-54 Skymaster and later aboard the prototype C-82 Packet. Large numbers of M22s were supplied to Great Britain, who named it the Locust. The British had developed the Hamilcar glider to carry their own Tetrach light tank, and this aircraft proved capable of carrying the Locust as well.

The Locust saw action only once, when a small number were landed by Hamilcar to take part in the Rhine crossing operation on 24 March 1945. Some Locusts were fitted with a special adaptor, which increased gun barrel length and muzzle velocity.

M24 CHAFFEE

The M24 was designed as part of a 'combat team' of light armoured vehicles, but saw little wartime service. Upgraded versions still serve today with some smaller armies.

Secondary armament was standard for a light tank with two built-in machine guns and another pintle-mounted machine gun for anti-aircraft defence.

The 75mm (2.95in) M6 main gun was originally a World War I French howitzer, which had been adapted and lightened for use in the B-25G bomber against shipping.

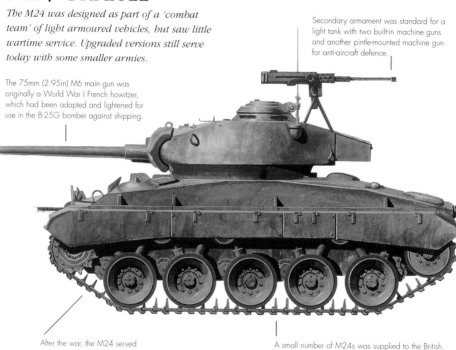

After the war, the M24 served with many nations, including France, Denmark and Taiwan.

A small number of M24s was supplied to the British, who named it Chaffee after General Adna R. Chaffee, the first commander of the US Armored Force.

The M24 had two engines and Hydramatic suspension, features developed for the M5. Many features of the M24 were used on post-war US tanks.

Armour thickness on the Chaffee ranged from only 9mm (0.35in) to 25mm (0.98in).

The M24 was fast and pleasant to drive, but did not have the armament or armour to take on heavy tanks.

The M24 had a cross-country speed of 40km/h (25mph), which was as fast as the maximum road speed of most heavy tanks.

UNITED STATES

In 1939 most light tanks (in short, almost all tanks) were equipped with main armament in the 37–40mm (1.46–1.57in) class. By 1942, it was recognized that this was now inadequate to defeat the armour of even other light tanks, and efforts were made in the United States and elsewhere to provide smaller tanks with

effective firepower. The M24 was developed by the US Army's Ordnance Department in conjunction with Cadillac, designers of the M5 light tank, and it incorporated a number of features of this earlier model, such as the

In the 1950s, M24s were used by French troops in Indochina.

The M24 was speedy and mobile with a good gun for its size.

M24 Chaffee

Powerplant:	Two 82kW (110hp) Cadillac 44T24 V-8 petrol engines
Performance:	The Chaffee had a maximum road speed of 56km/h (35mph) and a road range of 160km (100 miles)
Dimensions:	length: 5.48m (18ft); width: 2.97m (9ft 8in); height: 2.5m (8ft 2in)

twin Cadillac V-8 engines and Hydramatic suspension. Most of the M24, including the running gear and turret, was of completely new design.

The M24 was designed as part of a 'light combat team', or family of vehicles, that used the same chassis, including mortar and AA gun carriages. Most of these projects were cancelled, however, when the war ended. Versions that did see action included the M19 with twin 40mm (1.57in) AA guns and the M37 Howitzer Motor Carriage (HMC).

The M24 saw little wartime action, although it was rushed into service in Europe in 1945, where its high speed and reliability were appreciated, and took part in the battle for Okinawa in the Pacific. Post-war, the M24 saw much service with the United States and its allies and was to become the basis for the M41, M48 and M60 series of tanks.

UNITED STATES

M26 PERSHING

*The Pershing was America's only heavy tank to
enter service during the war and it saw limited
action in Europe and the Pacific in 1945. In
1946 the M26 was reclassified as a Medium
Tank. It saw much service in the Korean War.*

When fighting broke out in Korea in1950,
Pershings were quickly rushed to the theatre,
where they helped counter the advance of the
T-34s that had defeated lighter opposition.

The Pershing had a 90mm (3.5in) 53
calibres gun with a large muzzle brake.
This gun proved somewhat disappointing,
its penetrating ability inferior to that of the
Panther and Tiger.

The sloped armour, large
road wheels and torsion bar
suspension led the way to
post-war US tank designs
up to the M60 series.

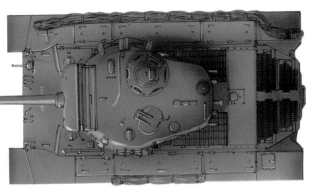

The Pershing fired two-part ammunition with a warhead and a propelling charge, which were loaded seperately.

The M26 formed the basis of a 'heavy combat team' of tanks, SP guns and recovery vehicles on the same chassis.

Versions of the M26, such as the T26E2 – with a 105mm (4.1in) howitzer – got as far as standardization (as the M45), but few were completed. Equipped with an improved M3A1 90mm (3.5in) gun, the M26A1 was a post-war development.

A 1942 programme to replace the M4 medium tank produced several pilot models – the T20, 22, 23, 25 and 26 – and led to the only successful US heavy tank of the war, the M26 Pershing. The T26E1 was selected, but had to be modified before it could be standardized. The transmission, engine cooling, electrical system and ammunition stowage were all improved, but Army Ground Forces did not want a heavy

An M26 Pershing waits to be barged across a river in Germany in 1945.

tank and tried to delay production. AGF rejected a test of the first T26E3s in December 1944, but then came the German breakthrough in the Ardennes. By February 1945, 20 were serving and there were 310 when peace came to Europe. The type was standardized in March 1945 as the M26

M26 Pershing

Powerplant:	373kW (500hp) Ford GAF V-8 petrol engine
Performance:	The M26 had a maximum road speed of 48km/h (30mph) and a road range of 161km (100 miles)
Dimensions:	length: 8.66m (28ft 3in); width: 3.51m (11ft 6in); height: 2.78m (9ft 1in)

The first 20 T26E3s arrived in Europe in January 1945 and were issued to the 3rd and 9th Armored Divisions.

Heavy Tank, and saw action at Okinawa in May. It was the first US tank to be named – General Pershing.

Here, at last, was a tank to confront the Tiger and Panther on equal terms, although the M3 90mm (3.5in) gun proved slightly inferior to the German '88s'. The M26A1 had the longer 90mm (3.5in) T15 gun; some were fitted with an elevation stabilizer. The gun fired single-part, not separate, ammunition and had a concentric recoil system. The British received a few Pershings for evaluation, but orders were cancelled at the war's end.

In total, 2432 were produced, most of which were the initial M26 model.

LVT-4 'WATER BUFFALO'

The US Marines developed a series of specialized amphibious tractors, or 'AMTRACs', to deliver troops to Pacific island beaches. The LVT-4 Water Buffalo was the most numerous model.

Initial LVT-4s had two large and two small glass windows at the front of the crew compartment, but these were replaced by a single armoured hatch on the version seen here, the LVT-4 Armoured Cab.

The LVT-4 had a crew of two (driver and commander) and could carry up to 24 Marines.

The ramp was operated by a winch and lowered by cables on each side of the cargo compartment.

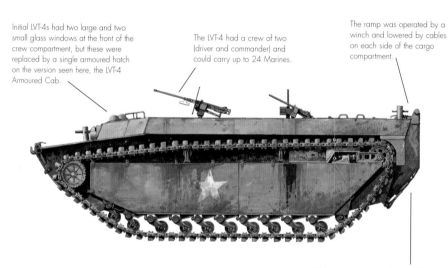

With its rear ramp, the LVT-4 could carry wheeled equipment such as Jeeps and light artillery pieces.

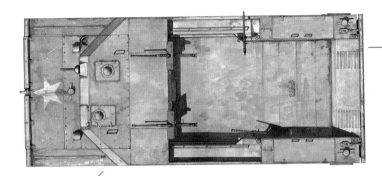

In the Pacific, the Marines valued the LVTs for their ability to cross coral reefs and carry them inland, which landing craft could not do.

The LVT-4 had the engine moved forward to behind the driver's compartment and a rear ramp fitted. This allowed much easier loading and safer disembarking under fire.

As well as a 7.6mm (0.3in) bow machine gun, the LVT-4 was fitted with up to four pintle-mounted machine guns, two of them of 12mm (0.5in) calibre.

The LVT-4 was powered in the water by cup-like grousers on the tracks, which propelled the vehicle at up to 12km/h (6.5mph).

UNITED STATES

173

The LVT-4 evolved from the earlier tracked landing vehicles LVT-1, -2 and -3, which in turn were descendants of the 'Alligator', a 1930s lightweight tracked amphibious vehicle designed by engineer Donald Roebling for rescue work in the Florida Everglades. In 1937, the US Marine Corps took an interest after an article on the

Packed with US Marines, LVT-2s and LVT-4s lead the assault on the Japanese island of Iwo Jima in 1945.

vehicle was published in *Life* magazine Following trials and modifications, 300 LVT (Landing Vehicle, Tracked) -1s were ordered as ship-to-shore cargo carriers. These were constructed by the Food Machinery Company (FMC) in California.

The LVT-2 was an improved model with the engine and drive train of the M2 light tank, but its central cargo compartment was hard to load and unload and was bisected by the drive shaft, restricting its use to troops and small teams. FMC solved these problems on the LVT-4 Water Buffalo, first delivered at the end of 1943, then followed by 8350 more, making it the most numerous of all the AMTRACs (amphibious tractors) produced. Most of these went to the US Army, which was preparing for the Normandy invasion, but in the end those few that saw action in Europe were used by the British.

In the Pacific, many were sunk by shellfire in the bloody Tarawa operation, and this revealed the need for armour-plated and better-armed versions.

An LVT-4 with shielded machine guns moves inland on Okinawa.

LVT-4

Powerplant:	187kW (250hp) Continental W670-9A, seven-cylinder, radial petrol engine
Performance:	The LVT-4 had a maximum road speed of 32km/h (20mph) and a road range of 480km (300 miles)
Dimensions:	length: 8.5m (27ft 10in); width: 3.25m (10ft 8in); height: 2.64m (8ft 9in)

UNITED STATES

175

LVT(A)-4

Experience at Tarawa in November 1943 showed the need for a more heavily armed version of the AMTRAC to support the troop carriers. Various light tank turrets were tried before the definitive LVT(A)-4 and -5, with the turret of the M8 howitzer, appeared in time for the Marianas campaign in the summer of 1944.

The LVT(A)-4 was armed with a 75mm (2.95in) howitzer in the complete turret of the M8 Howitzer Motor Carriage (HMC).

Some LVT(A)s carried rocket launchers on the rear hull, and there was a version with an E7 flame projector in place of the howitzer.

LVT(A)s were later modified with a rounded bow, a covered turret and new engine covers, and used in the Korean War.

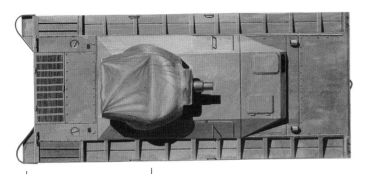

Early models like this one had no secondary armament, but the so-called 'Marianas model' had a bow gun and two machine guns on the turret rim.

The LVT(A)-4 was followed by the LVT(A)-5, which was identical but for a gun stabilization system that helped the AMTRAC fire accurately on the move.

Like the M8, the LVT(A)-4 had a power-operated open-topped turret, seen here with a canvas cover.

The LVT(A)-4s were designed to destroy enemy bunkers as they waded ashore. They were also used for fire support well inland.

UNITED STATES

177

After the near-disaster of the Tarawa invasion, in which many AMTRACs (Amphibious Tractors) were lost for the want of close-in fire support, the LVT Water Buffalo was redesigned to meet the requirement for a 'floating tank'. The resulting LVT(A)s were built from armour plate rather than mild steel and had one of a variety of tank or gun carriage turrets added

LVT(A)-4s come ashore at Okinawa in support of the troop-carrying 'AMTRACS'.

on top. The LVT(A)-4 replaced the M5 Stuart turret and 37mm (1.46in) cannon of the LVT(A)-2 with the complete turret of the M8 HMC (Howitzer Motor Carriage) and its 75mm (2.95in) howitzer. A canvas cover protected the open turret when not in action. Turreted versions carried buoyancy bags to compensate for the extra weight. In total, 1890 LVT(A)-4s were built in 1944–45.

A drawback of the LVT(A)-4 was that it was impossible to fire the main gun accurately while bobbing up and down in the waves, especially with hand traverse of the turret. The LVT(A)-5 therefore had power traverse and a gyro-stabilizer for the turret. The last of the original AMTANKs, it saw action in Korea.

LVT(A)-4

Powerplant:	187kW (250hp) Continental W670-9A, seven-cylinder, radial petrol engine
Performance:	The LVT(A)-4 had a maximum road speed of 40km/h (25mph) and a road range of 480km (300 miles)
Dimensions:	length: 7.9m (26ft 2in); width: 3.25m (10ft 8in); height: 3.09m (10ft 3in)

The LVT series was propelled through the water by the tracks, which had integral cup-shaped grousers. This eliminated the complexity and volume of the propeller and shaft used on other amphibious vehicles, but led to a rather low water speed.

An early LVT(A) mounted with an M5 Stuart turret heads for the beach at Saipan in 1944.

M7B1 PRIEST HOWITZER MOTOR CARRIAGE

The M7 Priest self-propelled howitzer (or
Howitzer Motor Carriage in US parlance) was
the main Allied mobile fire-support weapon
from 1942 to 1945. The M7B1 was based on the
chassis of the M4 Sherman medium tank.

The M7B1 had two operating
crew (a commander and a driver)
and a gun crew of five.

The Priest's armour was thin (a maximum of
25mm/0.98in) and good only against
small arms fire and shrapnel.

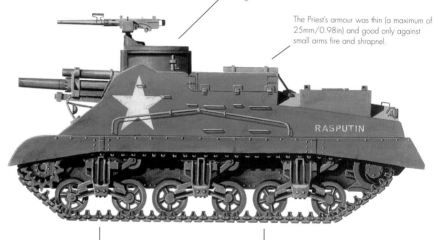

RASPUTIN

On the M7B1 hinged side plates were
added to protect the tips of the vertically-
stowed ammunition from small arms fire.

Some M7Bs were converted to Priest
Kangaroo personnel carriers and others to
mobile observation posts.

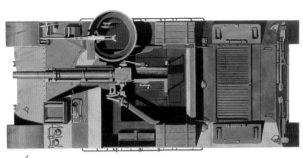

The US Army used Priests from November 1942 until war's end and in the Korean War, where the M7B2, with a raised gun mount to allow 65 degrees elevation, was the main version.

The 105mm (4.1in) gun was larger than that on any Allied tank, but was comparatively light for such a large hull. A total of 69 rounds of ammunition could be stowed within the vehicle.

The 'pulpit' commander's cupola mounted an 12mm (0.5in) machine gun for defence against aircraft and ambush. The Priest was not expected to fight the enemy at close range.

US Priests were used to the end of the war in northwest Europe, but British versions were replaced by Sextons early in the Normandy campaign.

UNITED STATES

181

UNITED STATES

The M7 self-propelled howitzers supplied mobile artillery support to the tank divisions that were equipping with the M3 medium tanks in 1941. The M3 chassis was roomy enough for a large gun and its crew, and was adapted as the basis for the M7 HMC (Howitzer Motor Carriage) in February 1942. The British ordered a massive 5500 as soon as they saw the prototype, but the US Army took priority and few could be spared. Those available by the end of 1942 played a major role in the

Positioned to give high-angle fire, an M7B1 fires at German positions across the Rapido River in Italy, 1944.

This preserved Priest shows the 'pulpit' commander's position that gave the M7B1 its name.

M7B1 Priest Howitzer Motor Carriage

Powerplant:	373kW (500hp) Ford GAA V-8 petrol engine
Performance:	The Priest had a maximum road speed of 42km/h (26mph) and a road range of 201km (125 miles)
Dimensions:	length: 6.2m (20ft 3in); width: 2.89m (9ft 5in); height: 2.54m (8ft 4in)

Battle of El Alamein, which saw the defeat of German forces in the desert. The name Priest, chosen as usual by the British, was a reference to the 'pulpit' commander's position. Later, the Sexton and Bishop gun carriages continued the ecclesiastical theme.

The tactical concept of the Priest was to provide heavy artillery support with indirect fire rather than direct assault on enemy positions, so its armour was thin. The M7B1 was built to the same specifications as the M7, but was based on the M4 Sherman chassis as the M3 was phased out by September 1943. The two versions could be distinguished by the three-piece nose of the M7 and the smooth cast nose of the M7B1.

Redundant Priests in Italy were often divested of their gun and converted to Priest Kangaroo armoured personnel carriers.

INFANTRY TANK MK II, MATILDA

The best British tank in the early part of the North African campaign, the Matilda II served throughout the war, the only British tank to do so. It was obsolescent by mid-1941 and sent to secondary theatres. Production continued until 1943, with a total of nearly 3000 produced.

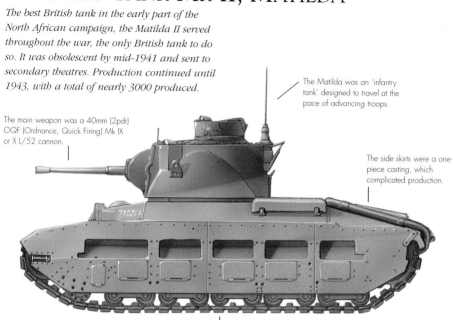

The Matilda was an 'infantry tank' designed to travel at the pace of advancing troops.

The main weapon was a 40mm (2pdr) OQF (Ordnance, Quick Firing) Mk IX or X L/52 cannon.

The side skirts were a one-piece casting, which complicated production.

The side skirts contained sand chutes to prevent track clogging. The prototypes had six, but series models had five to simplify manufacture.

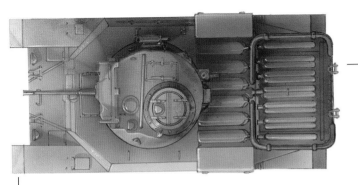

The Matilda II was powered by twin AEC diesel engines coupled to a five-speed gearbox. The Matilda III had twin Leyland petrol engines and a six-speed transmission.

UNITED KINGDOM

The Matilda was named after a cartoon duck character of the pre-war period.

The secondary armament was a single 7.7mm (0.303in) machine gun. On the Mk II, this was a Besa gun. A Bren gun was sometimes fitted for anti-aircraft defence.

The curved armour, which was up to 78mm (3in) thick on the lower front hull, was virtually impregnable to small calibre anti-tank guns.

185

UNITED KINGDOM

The A11 Matilda infantry tank of 1936 had been something of a failure with a crew of two and machine gun armament, though it was praised for its extremely good armour protection. By 1937, a successor was in development, which addressed the problems of armament and had room for a four-man crew. The first A12

An Australian Matilda drives ashore from a ship to join the fighting in Egypt. The type was well suited to the desert.

Matilda II was rolled out in 1938 and featured the standard 40mm (2pdr) cannon of the time. The many cast parts meant that production took time to reach its peak.

The Matilda II's combat debut came at Arras, France, in late May 1940, when they mounted a successful counterattack against Rommel's panzers. In the Western Desert they bettered all Italian tanks and were extremely important until the first battle of El Alamein in July 1942, when the Germans began to field the 88mm (3.46in) anti-tank gun, which could easily defeat the armour of the Matilda. By the second battle of El Alamein in October, better US designs became available in large numbers.

Attempts to mount larger guns were mostly unsuccessful, except for the Matilda III CS with a 76mm (3in) howitzer. Many obsolete Matildas were subsequently used in the Pacific by Australian forces, who developed some specialized versions, including flamethrowers. Matildas were also used as the first flail tanks for clearing mines.

Matildas helped train British crews for newer and better tanks.

Infantry Tank Mk II, Matilda

Powerplant:	Two 65kW (87hp) AEC six-cylinder diesel engines
Performance:	The Matilda II had a maximum road speed of 24km/h (15mph) and a road range of 257km (160 miles)
Dimensions:	length: 5.61m (18ft 5in); width: 2.59m (8ft 6in); height: 2.52m (8ft 3in)

UNITED KINGDOM

INFANTRY TANK MK III, VALENTINE I

The Valentine was one of the most reliable British tanks and was effective in supporting infantry in the Western Desert, but not against German panzers.

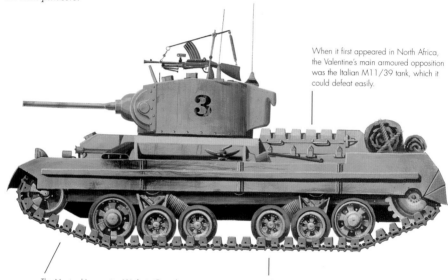

When it first appeared in North Africa, the Valentine's main armoured opposition was the Italian M11/39 tank, which it could defeat easily.

The Montreal Locomotive Works in Canada produced 1420 Valentines, most of which were supplied to the Soviet Army.

The Valentine was designed as an infantry tank, but was often used as a more free-ranging 'cruiser'.

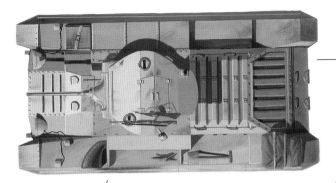

The Valentine III introduced a larger three-man turret with the commander's position moved towards the rear and provision for a loader, increasing the crew to four.

The Valentine was restricted to a 57mm (6pdr) gun because the turret ring could not mount a turret big enough to contain the breech of a more powerful gun.

The Valentine was built in 11 main variants and several specialized models, including flamethrowers, 'swimming' tanks and bridgelayers.

UNITED KINGDOM

189

UNITED KINGDOM

The Valentine was widely used for training; here Polish crews practice in Scotland, 1942.

war looming in Europe, a substantial order was made in July 1939 and by late 1940 the first examples were in service.

The 8th Army was equipped with many Valentines by mid-1941 and the type played a major role in fighting in the Western Desert. The Valentine suffered from the deficiencies of most British tanks of the period, namely poor firepower and armour protection in comparison to its opponents, but was one of the more reliable tanks because most of the mechanical problems of the A10 had been designed out.

One of the failings of the early models was the small two-man turret, which forced the gunner to take his eye off the target to reload the gun himself. Some Valentine IIIs were equipped with DD (Duplex Drive) equipment and side-skirts so that they could

Named Valentine because Vickers submitted its design to the War Office just before the deadline of 14 February 1938, the Infantry Tank Mk III was a development of the A10 Heavy Cruiser, already produced by the firm. With

'swim' ashore from landing-craft. By the time of the Normandy landings, the Valentine DDs were replaced by Sherman DDs, but they helped develop operational methods and train crews of the 79th Armoured Division.

Over 1400 Valentine Mk VIs were built by Canadian Pacific in Montreal and the great majority were supplied to the Russians, who later refitted many of them with a more useful Russian-made 76.2mm (3in) gun. The Valentine was reliable enough for use on the Eastern Front, but its narrow tracks proved

Infantry Tank Mk III, Valentine I

Powerplant:	97.7kW (131hp) AEC six-cylinder diesel engine
Performance:	The Valentine III had a maximum road speed of 24km/h (15mph) and a road range of 145km (90 miles)
Dimensions:	length: 5.41m (17ft 9in); width: 2.63m (8ft 7in); height: 2.27m (7ft 5in)

unsuitable in winter conditions. The Valentine's importance lay more in the numbers produced (8275) than in its quality. Valentines were supplied to Australia and New Zealand, where they were used mainly for training.

DD Valentines were the first British amphibious tanks, although they never saw combat.

Mk IVA Cruiser Tank

British army doctrine of the 1930s called for fast 'Cruiser' tanks and heavier 'Infantry' tanks. The Cruiser IV (or A13 Mk II) was one of the last of its breed, but led to the better Crusader. Cruiser IVs saw combat in France and in the early desert campaigns.

The unusual lozenge-shaped turret of the Cruiser came about from the additional armour. The original flat-sided turret of the Cruiser III was only 14mm (0.55in) thick at best.

The Cruiser IV had Christie suspension – named after the eccentric US inventor J. Walter Christie. This involved large road wheels without return rollers of complex suspension.

The commander's cupola had a split armoured hatch cover and a searchlight. Another searchlight was fitted at the front centre, but this was very vulnerable in action.

The Mk IVA had a Vickers machine gun in place of the Besa on the Mk IV.

The Cruiser Mk III was the precursor to the Mk IV and saw action in France and Libya. This photograph shows the original turret shape.

turret added 544 kg (1200 lb) to the weight, but did not greatly affect the performance or handling due to the high power-to-weight ratio provided by the Nuffield Liberty V-12 engine.

The v-section armour on the turret sides distinguished it from the Cruiser III and produced a 'spaced armour' effect, which killed the energy of a shell before it struck the turret proper. The A13 Cruiser had a high power-to-weight ratio and, despite the extra weight of the new armour, performance hardly suffered and the Mk IV was one of the fastest tanks of the war. The Mk IVA differed mainly in having a Besa machine gun, which became the standard secondary weapon on British tanks, in place of the Vickers gun of the Mk IV.

Also known by the ordnance designation A13 Mk II, the Cruiser Mk IV was an up-armoured version of the Cruiser Mk III (A13).

In early 1939 it had been decided that all Cruiser-type tanks should have a minimum armour thickness of 30mm (1.18in). The additional armour on the nose, glacis and

Cruiser IVs lie knocked out in the streets of Tobruk, Libya, which changed hands several times in 1941–42.

Mk IVA Cruiser Tank

Powerplant:	254kW (340hp) Nuffield Liberty V-12 petrol engine
Performance:	The Mk IVA had a maximum road speed of 46km/h (30mph) and a road range of 144km (90 miles)
Dimensions:	length: 6.02m (19ft 9in); width: 2.54m (8ft 4in); height: 2.59m (8ft 6in)

Most IVAs had an armoured mantlet for the main gun. The Mk IVCS was a version with a 94mm (3.7in) mortar in place of the 40mm (2pdr) OQF (Ordnance, Quick Firing) cannon. The 1st Armoured Division used the Cruiser Mk IV in France in 1940, and the 7th Armoured Division (the Desert Rats) used it in the Western Desert, where its high speed was valued.

After 1941, they were used mainly for training in the UK. Total production of 655 examples was split between prime contractor Nuffield, LMS, Leyland and English Electric.

UNITED KINGDOM

MK VI CRUISER TANK, CRUSADER I

Despite its faults, the Crusader was very important to British forces in North Africa. By May1943, the last were retired from front-line service, although special purpose versions (AA tanks, recovery vehicles and gun tractors) were in use after D-Day.

UNITED KINGDOM

The Crusader I had a 40mm (2pdr) gun, typical for the early war period but barely adequate against tank armour.

As first seen on some Mk IV Cruisers, additional armour was built up in front of the gun mantlet. The main armament and coaxial machine gun were elevated in a vertical slot in this armour.

When fitted, an auxiliary fuel tank at the rear gave the Crusader an extra 44km (27 miles) range.

Skirt guards covering the upper tracks were seen on most Crusaders used in the Western Desert.

The poorly ventilated front turret was removed from many Mk Is and this allowed the crew to be reduced to a more comfortable four, although the gunner's space was usually filled with more ammunition.

The Crusader I had poor ventilation and engine cooling and a troublesome gearbox.

The turret was of mixed riveted and welded steel construction. The thickest armour on the Crusader was 40mm (1.5in) and the thinnest only 7mm (0.27in).

The secondary armament of two 7.92mm (0.303in) Besa machine guns were fitted on a coaxial mount and in a fixed barbette on the forward hull.

One of the most distinctive British tanks of the war, the Crusader was also one of the least effective, suffering from a hasty development and an outmoded design concept. It began as a private venture by the Nuffield organization to create a 'heavy cruiser' version of its earlier Cruiser IV.

Trials of the Crusader were rushed, leading to many teething troubles during initial service.

As such, the Crusader, which was ordered in July 1939, had the same engine and turret, but was lengthened and had greater armour protection all round. As the political situation deteriorated, orders for 200 were quickly followed by another 200 and then a further 662. Up to 1943, 5300 were built. Abbreviated trials of the prototype revealed many problems, which became more apparent when the Crusader first saw combat in the Western Desert in June 1941. Some problems were solved – they had to be, as the Crusader was numerically one of

This early model lacks the upper track covers seen on Crusaders used in action.

Mk VI Cruiser Tank, Crusader I

Powerplant:	254kW (340hp) Nuffield Liberty V-12 petrol engine
Performance:	The Crusader I had a maximum road speed of 43km/h (27mph) and a road range of 160km (100 miles)
Dimensions:	length: 5.99m (19ft 8in); width: 2.64m (8ft 8in); height: 2.23m (7ft 4in)

the most important tanks in the theatre. The Mk III, available by mid-1942, corrected the Crusader's main weakness, its lack of firepower, by introducing the 57mm (6pdr) gun and was the main variant in service by the time of the Battle of El Alamein.

Nonetheless, the guns of the German panzers, not to mention the anti-tank guns, could usually pick off Crusaders at long range, despite their speed and small size.

UNITED KINGDOM

INFANTRY TANK MK IV, CHURCHILL IV

The Churchill was the main British-designed heavy tank of the mid-war years. It was slow and poorly armed, but effective when it did not have to face enemy armour. Over 5600 were built.

The Churchill IV was fitted with a 57mm (6pdr) gun, usually the OQF (Ordnance, Quick Firing) Mk V with its distinctive muzzle-end counterweight. This was a 'single-purpose' gun like the 40mm (2pdr), able to fire armour-piercing (AP) but not high-explosive (HE) rounds.

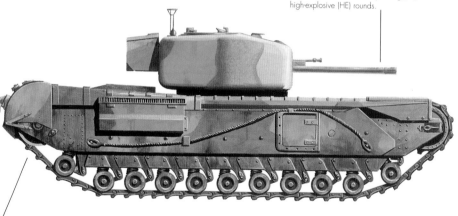

The Churchill IV, first produced in mid-1942, corrected many of the faults of the earlier models, which tended to affect minor components and the transmission system.

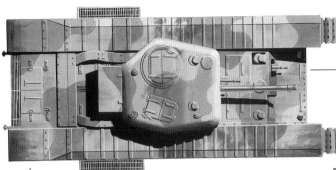

The Churchill had a wide hull and capacious interior, which made it suitable for conversion to a bridgelayer or engineer vehicle with a crew of up to seven men.

The Churchill's combat debut came on the abortive Dieppe raid in May 1942, when many Churchills failed to reach the beach, let alone support the infantry any distance inland.

The Churchill was well armoured, with a maximum thickness of 102mm (4in) on the Mk IV. The weight of the armour contributed to its low cross-country speed of only 12.8km/h (8mph).

Designed for carriage on narrow-gauge British railways, the Churchill was too narrow to accept the larger turret ring needed to mount a bigger gun.

UNITED KINGDOM

201

UNITED KINGDOM

Royal Air Force personnel undergo 'tank indoctrination' with a Churchill during training in Britain.

The Churchill was the last of the so-called 'Infantry' tanks built by the British. The design reflected World War I practice in that it had a long hull and tracks for trench crossing, and travelled across shell-churned ground at a speed that soldiers could match.

The specification was drawn up at the outbreak of war in September 1939 and a prototype was produced within five months. This featured two 40mm (2pdr) guns and two hull-mounted machine guns and carried a crew of seven. Because of its excessive weight and troublesome gearbox, the design was scaled down, the armament was halved and many detail changes were made.

By June 1941, the first of an order for 500 Churchill Is were rolled out. These, and the next batch of the same size, needed extensive modification before they could be issued to the troops.

Early Churchills could fire only armour piercing (AP) shells and had to rely on field artillery or naval ships for close support. At Dieppe this proved a distinct disadvantage as the tanks faced mainly fixed or soft targets, where high explosive rounds would have been more useful.

Infantry Tank Mk IV, Churchill IV

Powerplant:	261kW (350hp) Bedford twin six petrol engine
Performance:	The Churchill had a maximum road speed of 24km/h (15mph) and a road range of 144km/h (90 miles)
Dimensions:	length: 7.44m (24ft 5in); width: 2.74m (9ft); height: 3.45m (11ft 4in)

Despite its outmoded design, the Churchill proved a useful tank in Tunisia in 1943 and a year later in the Normandy landings. Many uses were found for Churchills other than as main battle tanks, particularly as mine-clearing, recovery and engineering vehicles.

A Churchill IV crosses a gully on the back of a pair of stacked Churchill bridging vehicles.

CHURCHILL AVRE

The Churchill AVRE was a multi-purpose armoured 'battle taxi' for engineers tasked with clearing or bridging obstacles. Armed with a large-calibre bomb projector, it often carried a secondary bridging or mine-clearing device, like the log carpet seen here.

This AVRE carries a log carpet, which would be dropped to aid in crossing boggy ground. Other AVREs were fitted with mine ploughs or rollers or bundles of logs for ditch crossing.

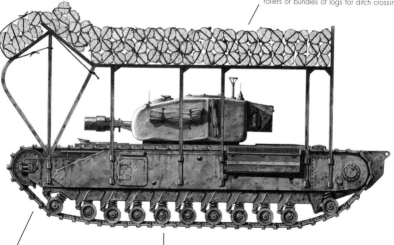

Wartime AVREs were mostly based on the Churchill Mks III and IV.

The capacious interior of the Churchill allowed for a party of about seven engineers to get close to bunkers, which could then be destroyed by satchel charges and other weapons.

Some Churchill AVREs carried large brushwood bundles, or 'fascines', which would be dropped into ditches or narrow water obstacles, compressing to fill the gap as the AVRE and following tanks drove over them. Pushed over the far side of wall defences, they could be used to reduce the drop for tanks climbing over the top.

The log carpet was released by setting off a small explosive charge from inside the tank. The plan view omits some of the 100 logs to allow a view of the turret.

The mortar shells, or 'flying dustbins', were not very accurate, but their blast would usually disable a gun emplacement and stun its occupants long enough for other tanks or infantry to finish the job.

The AVRE's main weapon was a 290mm (11.4in) 'recoiling spigot mortar' or 'petard mortar' It could fire a 18kg (40lb) demolition bomb a distance of about 73m (80 yards) at enemy bunkers or strongpoints.

UNITED KINGDOM

UNITED KINGDOM

The British/Canadian raid on the French port of Dieppe in May 1942 showed up the need for dedicated specialized tanks to clear beach obstacles and defences for the fighting vehicles in the first wave of an invasion. Many tanks (mostly Churchills) were caught on anti-tank obstacles and destroyed by crossfire from

This unarmed Mk IV AVRE mounts a Jeffries mine plough device.

fixed bunkers on the beach. Engineers could blow up some of the beach obstacles if they could reach them alive, and ditches and streams could be crossed with temporary bridges that could be laid by tanks.

Churchill AVRE

Powerplant:	261kW (350hp) Bedford twin six-cylinder (flat 12) petrol engine
Performance:	The AVRE had a maximum road speed of 24km/h (15mph) and a road range of 144km (90 miles)
Dimensions:	length: 7.44m (24ft 5in); width: 2.74m (9ft 0in); height: 4.24m (13ft 1in) to top of frame

A Mk IV AVRE bridgelayer goes through its paces in a training exercise.

From these requirements came the Churchill AVRE (Armoured Vehicle, Royal Engineers), which came in many forms but was basically an early form of armoured personnel carrier (APC) or infantry fighting vehicle (IFV), with a large mortar and some type of obstacle-clearing equipment. The roomy hull and large escape doors of the Churchill allowed a party of combat engineers to be carried and deposited on the beach or battlefield to clear obstructions.

In preparation for the Normandy landings, 180 conversions of standard Churchill IVs were made to AVRE tanks for the 79th Armoured Division. They proved their worth on 6 June 1944 and afterwards, when they saved many Allied lives. New versions were built after the war and the last were retired as late as 1965.

UNITED KINGDOM

207

CHURCHILL MK VII CROCODILE

*The Churchill Crocodile was a conversion of the
Churchill Mk VII adapted for the beach assault
role and used in the Normandy invasion as a
flamethrower and assault tank.*

The Churchill VII had
a new heavy cast and
welded turret with a
commander's cupola. ———

The Crocodile got its name because it
came on to the beach with a motion
suggestive of a crocodile crawling out
of the water.

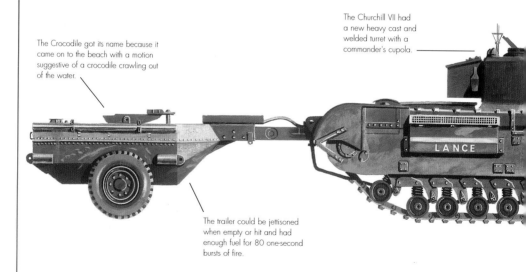

The trailer could be jettisoned
when empty or hit and had
enough fuel for 80 one-second
bursts of fire.

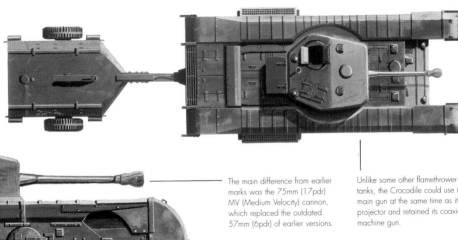

The main difference from earlier marks was the 75mm (17pdr) MV (Medium Velocity) cannon, which replaced the outdated 57mm (6pdr) of earlier versions.

Unlike some other flamethrower tanks, the Crocodile could use its main gun at the same time as its projector and retained its coaxial machine gun.

Although superficially similar to earlier models, the Churchill VII was of completely new construction. It had no hull frame, but was constructed from frameless armour plate that was joined to form a rigid structure.

UNITED KINGDOM

The Churchill Crocodile was developed for Operation Overlord, the invasion of Europe. Aware that the coast of France was fortified with anti-tank obstacles, bunkers and gun emplacements, the British formed the 79th Armoured Division to develop weapons and tactics for crossing those first, vital yards of beach. The 79th was led by General Percy

This 79th Armoured Division Crocodile is helping in the destruction of Belsen concentration camp in May 1945.

Hobart, and its converted tanks were known as 'Hobart's Funnies'. One was a conversion of the Churchill VII medium tank, and towed a trailer loaded with fuel. The Crocodile, of which 800 were made, replaced the hull

210

machine gun with a projector that emitted a jet of flame 73–110m (80–120 yards) long. This was fed under pressure by a pipe from the 6.5-tonnes (6.3-ton) armoured trailer.

On D-Day, the Crocodiles were used against bunkers and machine gun positions on the beach, and later as flamethrowers or conventional tanks, as the situation dictated.

A Churchill Crocodile with trailer eliminates a German-held building in Holland in 1945.

Churchill Mk VII Crocodile

Powerplant:	261kW (350hp) Bedford twin-six
Performance:	The Churchill VII had a maximum road speed of 20km/h (12.5mph) and a road range of 144km (90 miles)
Dimensions:	length: (without trailer) 7.44m (24ft 5in); width: 2.74m (9ft 0in); height: 3.45m (11ft 4in)

UNITED KINGDOM

A27M Cruiser Mk VIII, Cromwell V

*With its powerful Meteor engine, the Cromwell
was the fastest British tank of the war. The
Cromwell gave British tank crews the chance
to be at par with their German opponents.*

The main armament of the
Cromwell VI was a 75mm
(2.95in) OQF cannon.

The Cromwell's Meteor engine was a version of
the famous Merlin aero engine used in the Spitfire,
Lancaster and many other aircraft. The V-12
Meteor was the first truly reliable engine fitted to a
British tank and made the Cromwell the fastest
British tank of the war years.

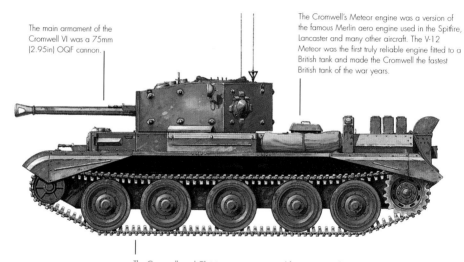

The Cromwell used Christie suspension, named for its inventor, the
American J. Walter Christie, who came up with many important
developments in tank design in the 1920s and 1930s.

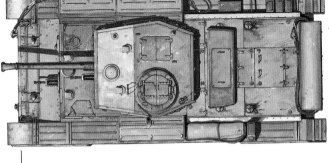

The Cromwell was a bit too fast for its suspension, which tended to wear too quickly. Later versions were de-tuned to reduce top speed in favour of overall maintainability.

Twenty three rounds were provided in the turret as ready rounds and up to 41 additional shells were stowed around the walls of the fighting compartment.

The Cromwell was the best British tank to see large-scale production and widespread service before the end of the war.

The Cromwell was well protected with frontal armour up to 76mm (3in) thick.

Cromwells advance through a village near Rotterdam in November 1944.

Built to a 1941 General Staff Requirement for a 'heavy cruiser' tank, the Cromwell took account of the Crusader, which had proved that speed was no substitute for armour and firepower. Fifty per cent heavier than the Crusader due to its increased armour, the Cromwell compensated by having the powerful Rolls-Royce Meteor engine.

The series of British Cruiser tanks that led to the Comet, the best British-designed wartime tank, began with the A24 or Cruiser Mk VII Cavalier, with a V-12 Nuffield engine in early 1942. Soon it was decided that the Rolls-Royce Merlin aero engine would be the best powerplant for the design. For tank use

A Cromwell Mk V practises in a training exercise in England.

A27M Cruiser Mk VIII, Cromwell V

Powerplant:	694kW (930hp) Rolls-Royce Meteor V12 petrol engine
Performance:	The Cromwell V had a maximum road speed of 61km/h (38 mph). The maximum range was 278km (173 miles)
Dimensions:	length: 6.42m (21ft 9in); width: 3.0m (10ft); height: 2.51m (8ft 3in)

the Merlin was renamed the Meteor, but until production could gear up, the Liberty engine of a World War I vintage would be used. Liberty versions were designated A27L Cruiser Mk VIII and named Centaur. The Liberty was chosen so that it could easily be exchanged for the Merlin/Meteor when it became available. Meteor-engined variants in turn became the A27M Cromwell.

UNITED KINGDOM

215

UNITED KINGDOM

Production began at Leyland Motors in January 1943 and was soon followed by the Cromwells II and III, all with the 57mm (6pdr) gun. The Mk IV of late 1943 introduced a 75mm (2.95in) gun, used until the 1945 Mk VIII sported a 95mm (3.74in) close-support howitzer.

The Centaur III was the best of the Liberty-engined models, having a 75mm OQF Mk II gun, a lightened version of the 17pdr (76mm) gun used in the Sherman Firefly. When sufficient Meteors were available, many Centaur IIIs were converted into the Cromwell IV.

By the time of the Normandy landings on 6 June 1944, British tank regiments were mainly equipped with the American Sherman, but the Cromwell still saw

A whitewashed Cromwell heads for the front in Belgium, January 1945. The Cromwell was one of the fastest wartime tanks.

considerable action with the 7th Armoured Division in Europe. The effective 17pdr gun had a number of teething troubles, but these were cured in time for the Normandy invasion, when Cromwell IIIs played an important role on the British beaches and in the following weeks of hard fighting against German armour and fortified positions in northern France.

The Cromwell was the main equipment of the British Armoured Division's Armoured Reconnaissance Regiments and of the 7th Armoured Division. It only served in northwest Europe (at least in World War II) and was not used in Italy or in the Middle or Far East. The Cromwell could hold its own against opponents such as the Panzer III and IV, but was still found wanting against the heavily armoured Panther and Tiger.

This Cromwell Mk VI is preserved at the Tank Museum at Bovington in England.

Variants included the Cromwell ARV (Armoured Recovery Vehicle) and the Cromwell OP mobile artillery observation post. From the Cromwell developed the Comet, which saw limited action before the war's end and considerable service post-war. During the Normandy campaign a version known as the Cromwell 'Prong' was created by fitting a Cullen hedge cutter device. Other versions included the Cromwell OP mobile observation post with a dummy gun and additional radio equipment.

UNITED KINGDOM

CRUISER MK VIII, CROMWELL VI

*The Cromwell VI was a version of the interim
Centaur III tank re-engined with the famous
Meteor engine. The combination of this
powerplant and an effective long-barrelled
75mm gun created one of the best Allied tanks.*

The turret armour could not be
described as well-shaped. On
most models it was bolted
together. Vehicles with welded
armour had a 'w' designation
after the mark number.

The main armament of the Cromwell
VI was a 75mm (2.95in) OQF
cannon, backed up by two 7.92mm
(0.31in) Besa machine guns (one
hull mounted, one co-axial).

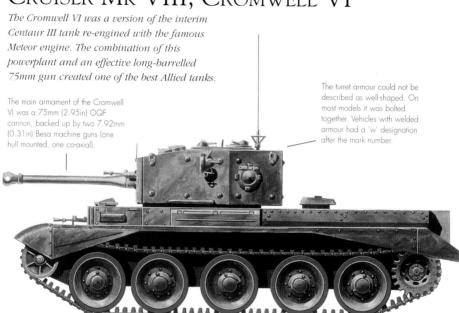

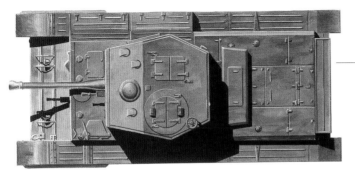

The Cromwell had a Merritt-Brown gearbox. This worked by slowing the track on one side while speeding up the track on the other, giving very smooth turns.

The Cromwell's armour was up to 76mm (3in) on the turret front. Some models had appliqué armour plates that boosted this to 101mm (3.9in).

The driver had a round front view port that was usually open when travelling. When in battle he looked through a glass viewing block.

UNITED KINGDOM

219

M4A4 SHERMAN VC FIREFLY

*Marrying the famous M4 Sherman's hull and
running gear with the best British anti-tank gun,
the Firefly was the British Army's most effective
tank at the time of the Normandy invasion.*

As was the practice of the time,
the British named the M4 after an
American general (in this case,
Civil War general William
Tecumseh Sherman, famous for
the quotation 'War is Hell'). The
Americans subsequently adopted
the name.

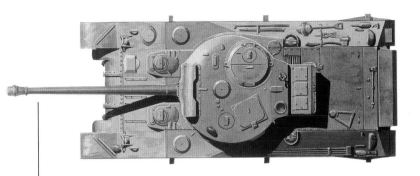

The British gave the Sherman family its own designations, namely the Sherman II (M4A1), Sherman III (M4A2), Sherman IV (M4A3) and Sherman V (M4A4). Suffix letters denoted the main armament fitted, C indicating the 76mm (17pdr) Ordnance, Quick Firing gun.

The Sherman V was based on the late-model M4A4 Sherman hull with a welded superstructure and three-part cast nose piece.

United Kingdom

The M4 medium tank was the most important US tank of the war, and the best, most numerous tank in British service. M4 Sherman Mk Is were used at El Alamein in October 1942 and later versions were introduced as they became available.

Existing British tanks could not take a turret large enough to mount the 76mm

The Firefly was more effective against German tanks than any US Sherman.

(17pdr) anti-tank gun, which was designed for both tank and anti-tank use. In the Sherman, the gun was fitted by mounting it on its side and adapting it for left-hand loading. The prototype, dubbed the 'Firefly', was ready in November 1943 and priority production was ordered in February 1944. This was too late for many to be available for D-Day, so one 'Firefly' was issued per troop of regular 75mm (2.95in) Shermans. It was the only British tank able to meet the German Panther and Tiger I on roughly equal terms, with a gun more accurate and longer-ranged than previously, able to penetrate 120mm (4.7in) armour at 500m (1500ft).

In combat, the three 'regular' Shermans distracted the enemy while the Firefly got

M4A4 Sherman VC Firefly

Powerplant:	298kW (400 hp) Continental nine-cylinder radial piston
Performance:	The Firefly had a maximum road speed of 40km/h (25mph) and a range of 193km (120 miles)
Dimensions:	length 5.89m (19ft 4in); width 2.62m (8ft 7in); height 2.75m (9ft)

into a good firing position. In general, two Shermans were lost for each Panther or Tiger destroyed, but German industry could not make up their losses by mid-1944, while nothing stopped US and British production lines. By early 1945, most British tank troops in Europe were equipped with Fireflies.

With its long 17pdr gun, the Firefly (centre) was easily distinguished from other versions of the Sherman.

UNITED KINGDOM

SHERMAN V CRAB II

The Sherman Crab was one of the most effective of the specialized British-modified 'funnies' built for the Normandy invasion in 1944. By flailing the ground with chains, the Crab detonated anti-tank and anti-personnel mines and marked safe lanes for other vehicles to follow. The Crab II had modifications to make it more suitable for use beyond the beaches.

At the rear of the Crab tanks were station-keeping devices and lane-marker dispensers so that the correct parts of the beach were swept and the clear lanes were kept to by the other vehicles.

The Sherman V had a 75mm (2.95in) M3 gyro-stabilized gun. The gun could fire both armour-piercing (AP) and high explosive (HE) shells.

Most wartime Shermans had VVSS (Vertical Volute Spring Suspension). Late models had HVSS (Horizontal Volute) suspension with a prominent cylinder and four bogey wheels on each unit.

The Chrysler Multibank engine was created by fixing five car engines to a single crankshaft.

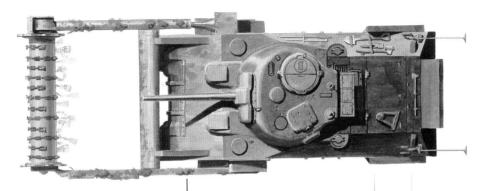

The M4A4 had a welded hull
with a three-part cast nose piece.

The Crab II had a contour-following device,
which was basically an extra weight on the
left-hand arm that forced the flail rig into dips
in the ground.

UNITED KINGDOM

The M4 Sherman spawned an astonishing number of variants: assault guns, rocket launchers, flame-throwers and bridgelayers. Some of the most unusual were created by the British for the specialized business of crossing the few yards of heavily defended beach on the Normandy coast. One of these was the

A Sherman Crab working with US troops approaches a minefield in Germany in 1945.

Sherman 'Crab', which was equipped with a mine 'flail'. This device was powered by a shaft drive from the tank's engine and was basically a rotating drum, to which was fixed

The Crab thrashed the ground with its flail chains, detonating enemy land mines.

Sherman V Crab II

Powerplant:	276kW (370hp) Chrysler WC multibank petrol engine
Performance:	The Sherman V had a maximum road speed of 40km/h (25mph) and a road range of 240km (150 miles) without flail
Dimensions:	length: 8.73m (28ft 7in); width: 3.25m (8ft 7in); height: 2.74m (9ft)

43 heavy chains that would thrash the beach and detonate any mines buried beneath the surface. The danger to tanks was from mines exploding directly beneath the tracks, so the shrapnel from nearby explosions was not a threat to the tank itself.

These vehicles were almost exclusively developed for use by the British 79th Armoured Division, and their use on the Normandy beaches on D-Day was one of the reasons for the relatively low casualties and good progress made by the British and Canadians in comparison with the high casualties of the US forces.

Later in 1944, the Crab II was used for dealing with inland minefields on rough terrain where mines could be missed. The main difference was a contouring device that kept the chains in contact with the ground when the terrain was rough.

UNITED KINGDOM

227

AEC Mk III Armoured Car

The AEC armoured cars were heavily armed and effective vehicles, packing the weaponry of a heavy tank. They were adaptable to larger guns as these became available.

The AEC III was heavily armed for an armoured car: its turret came from the Valentine tank.

F 88913

The AECs had selectable two- or four-wheel drive and steering with front-wheel drive used only for road travel.

The AEC Mk III had the 75mm (2.95in) M3 gun used on American medium tanks such as the M3 and many M4 Shermans. The secondary armament was a coaxial 7.92mm (0.31in) Besa machine gun.

After the war, some AEC IIIs were supplied to Belgium for its reconnaissance regiments. Total production of the three models was 629 vehicles.

Camouflage netting was applied to the turret of this AEC Mk III. Local foliage is threaded through the netting to provide some concealment in wooded terrain.

One of the few faults of this car was its high profile and angular appearance, which made it hard to conceal in the observation role.

UNITED KINGDOM

229

UNITED KINGDOM

Designed (and built) by a bus manufacturer without any official requirement, the AEC armoured cars proved to be the equal of many tanks of their day and served with distinction in North Africa and Europe. In 1941, the AEC (Associated Engineering Company) of Southall, West London-built an armoured car

An AEC II fires its 57mm (6pdr) gun during fighting for Tripoli in Libya.

based on information they had gleaned on fighting in North Africa. This Mk I car was virtually a wheeled tank, with heavy armour, a powerful engine and a 40mm (2pdr) gun, equivalent to that used by most tanks in the

This AEC III was one of many provided to Yugoslav partisans late in the war.

AEC Mk III Armoured Car

Powerplant:	78kW (105hp) AEC A195 six-cylinder diesel engine
Performance:	The AEC III had a maximum road speed of 58km/h (38mph) and a road range of 400km (250 miles)
Dimensions:	length: 5.61m (18ft 5in); width: 2.70m (8ft 11in); height: 2.69m (8ft 10in)

desert. Armament was increased on subsequent models in parallel with developments in tank guns. The AEC Mk II was given a three-man electrically traversed turret and a 57mm (6pdr) gun, but the Mk III had a 75mm (2.95in) M3 cannon. This was an exceptionally large gun for an Allied armoured car, and the high speed of the AEC made it valuable as a hit-and-run weapon, especially in North Africa. In general, the AEC IIIs served with the heavy troops of armoured car companies in northwest Europe, providing fire support when needed for the lighter Daimlers and Humbers. Later, the AECs saw most service in Italy and a number were supplied to Yugoslav partisans.

T17E1 STAGHOUND I

The Staghound was built in the United States, but used entirely by British and Commonwealth forces during the war. It was powerful, fast and well armed.

The Staghound I's main armament was a 37mm (1.46in) cannon. The later Mark III had a 75mm (2.95in) gun, which was much more effective against armoured targets.

The Staghound had stowage hooks for extra fuel containers and crew equipment such as bedrolls and tools.

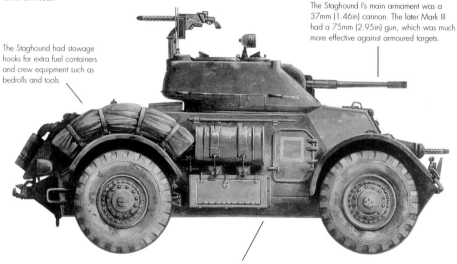

An advantage of armoured cars over tanks is that an entry/escape hatch can be fitted in the lower fuselage side.

After the war, Staghounds were supplied to various nations, including Denmark, India and South Africa, and remained in service for some years with the British Army itself.

The crew of five had three 7.62mm (0.303in) Browning machine guns in addition to the main gun. One was pintle-mounted on the turret roof, another was coaxial with the main gun, and the third was in the lower hull.

UNITED KINGDOM

233

UNITED KINGDOM

The Staghound was a US design for a heavy 'armored' car that was never used by US forces, all production going to Britain and Commonwealth forces. The US Army had seen how the 'Desert Rats'

The Staghound was faster and better armed than most light tanks.

made use of armoured cars in the Western Desert, and ordered two vehicles built, the

Ford T17 6x6 (six wheels, six-wheel drive) and the Chevrolet T17E1 4x4. The British saw the potential of the 4x4 and ordered an initial 300, although the Americans changed their own requirements and concentrated on other areas of development.

By the end of 1942, the first examples were shipped to Britain, and then issued to British, Canadian, Belgian, Indian and New Zealand units as the Staghound Mk I. The Staghound, with its high speed, good range,

T17E1 Staghound I

Powerplant:	72kW (97hp) GMC 270 six-cylinder petrol engine
Performance:	The Staghound I had a maximum road speed of 89km/h (55mph) and a road range of 724km (450 miles)
Dimensions:	length: 5.49m (18ft); width: 2.69 m (8ft 10in); height: 2.36m (7ft 9in)

thick armour and hydraulically traversed turret, was a popular and effective weapon. It was adaptable for a number of uses, including anti-aircraft (the Staghound AA with twin 12.7mm/0.5in guns) and anti-tank (Staghound Mk III with a Crusader turret and 75mm/2.95in gun).

The cast turret of a Staghound I is shown here before mounting.

UNITED KINGDOM

235

RAM KANGAROO

The Ram was a Canadian development of the M3 Lee/Grant with a new cast hull and turret. In a number of respects, it was superior to the similar Sherman, but did not see combat service as a battle tank. Many were converted to Ram Kangaroo personnel carriers.

The name Ram came from the family crest of the head of the Canadian armoured forces.

The Ram strongly resembled the M4 Sherman then under development in the United States, but it seems that the similarity was coincidental, both designs being adaptations of the same chassis to the same specification.

The Ram had a 7.62mm (0.3in) Browning hull machine gun in a limited-traverse turret on the front upper hull. This was retained on the Kangaroo APC version.

The first 50 armed versions were built as the Ram Mk I with a 40mm (2pdr) gun. The Ram Mk II was the main version with a 57mm (6pdr) gun. There were 1094 Ram IIs.

CANADA

CANADA

Canadian troops prepare for battle in a Ram Kangaroo in Holland, early 1945.

On the outbreak of war in September 1939, Britain looked to the Empire to supply what war materiel it could to supplement its own hard-pressed industries. The only Commonwealth nation with the heavy industrial base to begin armoured vehicle production was Canada, and railway engineering firms were soon hard at work producing Valentines for British and Canadian use.

A heavier tank was needed and rights were purchased to licence-build the US M3 (Lee/Grant) tank. However, its sponson-mounted gun arrangement was outmoded and it was therefore decided to adapt the basic chassis and running gear with a locally designed hull and turret.

The result was the Cruiser Tank Ram Mk I mounting a 40mm (2pdr) gun, the first of which was rolled out by the Montreal Locomotive Works in June 1941. Production of the Ram Mk II began in late 1941 and soon began to equip Canadian armoured divisions on their way to Europe. The Ram Mk II had a gyro-stabilized main gun of British design.

As a battle tank, the Ram never saw combat due to the availability of the Sherman by mid-1943. Instead, the Ram was developed for other purposes, including the Sexton SP gun and the Ram Kangaroo, which was one of the first fully tracked armoured personnel carriers (APCs) in use anywhere.

The conversion was made by removing the turret and installing rudimentary seating for up to 11 troops in battle order, and adding hand-grips on the hull to aid mounting and dismounting.

The Kangaroo was widely used by the armoured troop carrier battalions of the 79th Armoured Division in north-west Europe in 1944–45.

Ram Kangaroo

Powerplant:	254kW (340hp) Continental R-975-EC2 nine-cylinder radial petrol engine
Performance:	The Ram Kangaroo had a maximum road speed of 40km/h (25mph) and a road range of 232km (144 miles)
Dimensions:	length: 5.79m (19ft); width 2.76m (9ft 1in); height: 2.67m (8ft 9in)

CANADA

239

T-26A

The most numerous tank in Soviet service by the time of the German invasion, the T-26 was copied from an early Vickers design. Although ineffective against serious opposition, the T-26 gave the Soviet Union important experience of mass production and over 12,600 were built.

The T-26A was armed with one 37mm (1.46in) cannon and a 7.62mm (0.3in) DT machine gun in the other turret.

The T-26 had a system for internal communication using throat microphones.

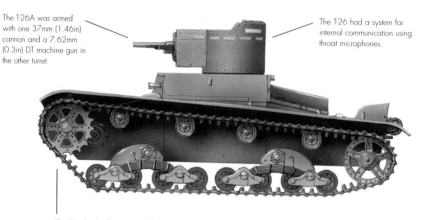

The T-26 had a front-mounted five-speed gearbox, which was connected to the engine by a drive shaft running under the crew compartment.

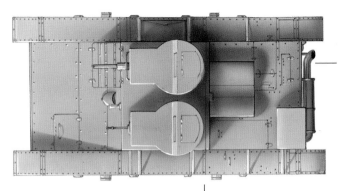

The GAZ engine was a licence-built version of an Armstrong Siddeley eight-cylinder powerplant. The original Six Ton Tank had a 65kW (87hp) four-cylinder engine.

One of the best features of the T-26 was a firewall between the engine and the fighting compartment, a feature lacking on many early 1930s tanks.

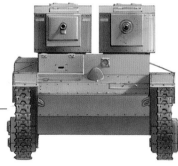

The suspension design of the Vickers Six Ton Tank influenced that of the US M2 and M3 light tanks, which in turn was adapted for the M3 Lee and M4 Sherman medium tanks.

SOVIET UNION

241

The British Vickers Six Ton Tank of 1928 had many novel features and was purchased by several nations, though not Britain. The design was widely copied, and the Soviet Union produced a slightly modified version, the T-26 Model 1931, or T-26A. This had an air-cooled rear-mounted petrol engine, a distinctive track layout, which sloped downwards to the rear, and leaf spring suspension. Like the Vickers tank, the T-26A had dual side-by-side turrets, equipped either for the infantry support role with two machine guns, often of different calibre, or as an 'artillery tank' with a gun of 27mm (1in) or 37mm (1.46in) in

The T-26 was extremely numerous but obsolescent by 1941.

T-26

Powerplant:	68kW (91hp) GAZ T-26 eight-cylinder petrol engine
Performance:	The T-26 had a maximum road speed of 28km/h (17 mph) and a road range of 200km (124 miles)
Dimensions:	length: 4.8m (15ft 9in); width: 2.44m (8ft 0in); height: 2.33m (7ft 8in)

The Russians copied and improved the British Six Ton Tank to produce the T-26S.

one turret. Command versions mounted the radio in the commander's left-hand turret, and the large frame aerial was mounted on the superstructure.

The Model 1933, or T-26B, dropped the cumbersome two-turret arrangement and had a single cylindrical turret with a 37mm (1.46in) cannon or a 45mm (1.77in) gun (T-26B-1). After the T-26 saw action in Manchuria, production switched from riveted to welded armour on the Model 1937, or T-26S. The new turret of the T-26S was retrofitted to many early models. Against the Chinese, the T-26 performed reasonably well, but the Finns proved tougher opposition in 1939/40.

The T-26 was the most numerous Soviet tank in June 1941, but was outclassed by the German tanks and tank crews, and their numbers had dwindled by early 1942.

T-28

*The first medium tank of Soviet design, the T-28
was influenced by German and British designs.
It was intended to assault enemy fortifications,
but by the time of the German invasion, it was
up against well-armed, manoeuvrable and fast
tanks that could exploit its weak spots.*

The T-28 had a cylindrical turret
mounting the main 76.2mm
(3in) gun and a machine gun
on a ball mounting.

The ball-mounted machine gun faced to
the rear on early T-28s, but later
models had an ammunition bustle at
the turret rear and the machine gun
was relocated to the front quarter.

The T-28's many wheels and long ground footprint gave
it a good trench-crossing ability. Unfortunately this was
not needed, as it was used mainly in the defensive role.

The engine compartment was at the rear of the
T-28, with the crew of six concentrated in the
fighting and driver's compartments at the front.

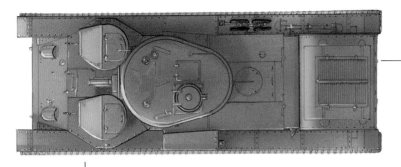

The M-17L was a Soviet version of the American Liberty aero engine that was developed at the end of World War I.

The T-28 was designed as a 'breakthrough tank' to mount frontal assaults on the enemy. With three turrets firing simultaneously, it could bring a heavy weight of fire on the target as it approached.

The T-28 had a high silhouette, which made it easy to spot and hit from a distance.

The T-28C had frontal armour increased to as much as 80mm (3.14in), which was very heavy for a pre-war tank. The T-28E had additional side armour panels.

SOVIET UNION

The first Soviet medium tank was influenced by German tanks that had been tested at Kazan in the early 1930s. The T-28, which appeared in 1933, had three cannon turrets: a central turret with a short-barrelled 76.2mm (3in) Model 1927/32 cannon and two small turrets mounting 45mm (1.77in) guns on the forward hull.

Early models replaced one of the 45mms with a 7.62mm (0.3in) DT machine gun. The

Although it possessed some good features, the T-28 was a failure in serious combat.

T-28A was produced until 1938, when the T-28B appeared with a more powerful L/10 gun. One advantage of the T-28 was its forward centre of gravity, which aided obstacle crossing.

In combat, during the Spanish Civil War and against Finland in 1939, it performed poorly, however. Armour was thin, at between 10 and 30mm (0.39–1.1in), and though the T-28E version had extra appliqué armour panels on the sides, these did little to help when the tank was faced by more mobile AFVs. Although having some shock value against enemy emplacements and troops, it was useless in open warfare.

The T-28 owed much to British infantry tank designs, apart from the multiple turrets.

T-28

Powerplant:	373kW (500hp) M-17L V-12 petrol engine
Performance:	The T-28 had a maximum road speed of 37km/h (23mph) and a road range of 190km (118 miles)
Dimensions:	length: 7.44m (24ft 5in); width: 2.8m (9ft 5in); height: 2.82m (9ft 3in)

SOVIET UNION

T-35B

The T-35 was an extraordinary 'land battleship' with no fewer than five gun turrets. It was mainly used for parades rather than on the battlefield. Total production was 55 of the model illustrated and six more with a conical turret.

The main turret contained a 76.2mm (3in) howitzer, and mounted a large radio aerial around its circumference.

The secondary turrets were in fact the turrets of light tanks, from the far more useful BT-5.

The crew of 11 was more akin to that of a World War I tank, and its members communicated by internal telephone.

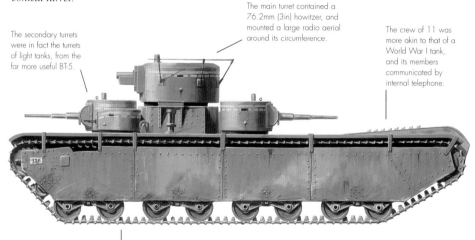

The T-35B was unmanoeuvrable but, more surprisingly, thinly armoured with a maximum thickness of only 30mm (1.18in). It weighed 45 tonnes (44.2 tons), far more than any pre-war tank.

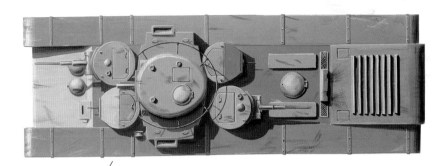

Beside each 37mm/1.46in
(or 45mm/1.77in) turret was
another containing a 7.6mm
(0.3in) DT machine gun.

The main armament was a 76.2mm (3in)
howitzer, the heaviest tank gun seen at that
time, backed up with a pair of 37mm
(1.46in), later 45mm (1.77in), turrets
mounted fore and aft. These were each
equivalent to or better than the armament
of any Western tank.

Despite the obsolescence of the multi-turret
concept, two of the designs tested as the
T-35B's potential successor in 1939 had twin
turrets and multiple machine guns. They lost
out to the conventional KV-1 design.

One of the most extraordinary, and heaviest, tanks to be used in the war, the T-35 'land battleship' was inspired by British experimental tanks of the 1920s, the plans of which the Soviets acquired surreptitiously. First displayed at the May Day parade in Moscow in 1933, the

A T-35B captured in 1941 is an object of curiosity to a German infantryman.

prototype T-35 caused great interest in the West, although no nation bothered to copy many of its features. The T-35 was designated a 'penetration tank', its role to lead lighter tanks and infantry into the assault, defending itself from all directions in the process.

Given the difficulty of moving the T-35 by rail, and its own limited range, it served with only one unit, the 5th Heavy Tank Brigade, whose role was the defence of Moscow. This also allowed T-35s to make their annual appearance at May Day parades in increasing numbers as production got under way.

The T-35 was noted in the Russo-Finnish war, and in the winter of 1941 saw combat outside Moscow, where several were

T-35B

Powerplant:	298kW (400hp) M-17M V-12 petrol engine
Performance:	The T-35B had a maximum road speed of 30km/h (18.6mph) and a road range of 160km (100 miles)
Dimensions:	Length: 9.72m (31ft 11in); width: 3.20m (10ft 6in); height: 3.43m (11ft 4in)

captured, having run out of fuel. At least one was taken to Germany for thorough testing. The main effect of tanks like the T-35 was to convince the Germans (erroneously) of the backwardness of Russian tank design in the last years of peace.

The T-35B seemed an impressive piece of war machinery in the 1930s but somewhat comical in hindsight.

BT-7

The BT-7 was one of the best tanks of the late 1930s, being fast, manoeuvrable and well armed for its day. Although obsolescent by 1941, many of its features were adopted by the T-34 and other important Soviet tanks.

The main armament was a 45mm (1.7in) M-32 cannon, backed up by a pair of 7.62mm (0.3in) DT machine guns.

A proportion of the BT-7s were equipped as command tanks with radio and a radial aerial around the turret.

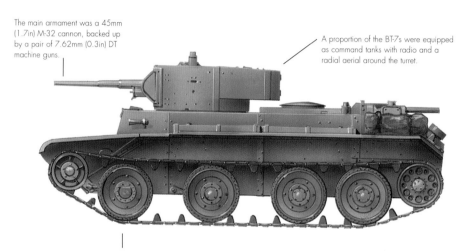

The BT tanks could run on the road without tracks. When this was done, the power was transmitted to the rear road wheels and the front wheels could be turned for steering. The Soviet Union never used this capability in combat.

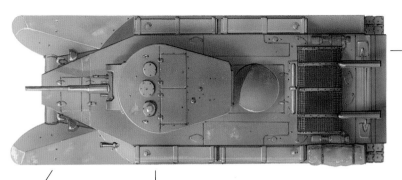

Several specialized versions of the BT-7 were created, including bridge-laying tanks and a smoke dispenser variant.

The initial BT-7's armour was quite thin at between 6 and 22mm (0.2–0.86in), but this was increased on the BT-7M.

The BT-7 was fitted with the same cylindrical turret as the T-26 tank of 1931.

The main legacy of eccentric American designer J. Walter Christie was his efficient suspension system with large road wheels that touched the top tracks. Russia made the most use of Christie's design from the BT series up to the present day.

A Soviet propaganda photo shows a BT-7 leading assault troops during a training exercise.

In 1930 the Soviet Union sought to modernize its tank forces and bought two examples of US inventor J. Walter Christie's M1931 light tank for study. Christie's tanks were never adopted in the USA, but their design, particularly the suspension, influenced the Soviets for years. The M1931 was copied as the BT-1 (Bystrochodya Tank, or fast tank) with machine gun armament, followed by the BT-2 with a 37mm (1.46in) cannon. The larger BT-5 with a 47mm (1.85in) gun appeared in 1932, seeing action in Spain and Manchuria.

The definitive BT-7 appeared in 1935 with a 45mm (1.77in) gun, a new gearbox and greater fuel capacity. The BT-5 and -7 had a petrol-driven V-12 aero engine. The BT-7 was lightly armoured and highly powered and as a result was fast and used in the 'cavalry' role. Following experience in Spain, armour was increased on the BT-7M (or BT-8). This also had a new diesel inline engine and sloped glacis plate, which was later adapted for the T-34.

This BT-7 has been preserved as a memorial in Russia.

BT-7

Powerplant:	336kW (450hp) M-17T V-12 petrol engine
Performance:	The BT-7 had a maximum road speed of 86km/h (53mph) and a road range of 250km (155 miles)
Dimensions:	length: 5.68m (18ft 8in); width: 2.43m (8ft); height: 2.28m (7ft 6in)

The BT-7M was effective against the Japanese and in Eastern Poland (occupied by the Soviet Army in late 1939), but in the Russo-Finnish war the deficiencies of poor armour and crew training became apparent.

In June 1941, the BT-7s were no match for the German tanks. Many were lost at the start of Operation Barbarossa, and the BT-7 and BT-7M had all but vanished by the end of the year.

SOVIET UNION

255

SOVIET UNION

KV-1A

The KV-1A was a modern design in 1941, but not very reliable and too heavy. Many KV-1As were lost to dive-bomber attacks and more to minor mechanical problems that could not be fixed in the field.

The KV-1A's main armament was a 76.2mm (3in) 1940 (F34) cannon. The secondary armament consisted of three 7.62mm (0.3in) DT machine guns (one coaxial, one in hull, and one in the rear of the turret).

Some KV-1 models produced in 1942 had an 85mm (3.34in) gun and thicker armour, making them heavier and 6km/h (4mph) slower.

The machine gun in the rear of the turret protected the tank from attack by grenades or satchel charges.

The KV-1A weighed 47.5 tonnes (46.7 tons), even more than the massive T-35B.

During 1940, the original L-11 gun was replaced by this longer-barrelled gun then used on the T-34.

The KV-1As had a high ammunition capacity of up to 114 rounds, which was fortunate because a complex gun sighting system meant that many shots were wasted.

The remarkable total of 900 KV-1As were produced between July and December 1941, even though the factory had to be moved bodily to a site east of the Ural Mountains.

SOVIET UNION

In 1938, the Soviets needed a modern heavy tank to replace the obsolete multi-turreted models then in service. Two of the three designs put forward had at least two turrets, but one had only a single turret and was thus able to carry heavy armour and armament. Two examples of this were

The 1942 model KV-1 had a heavier turret and a better 76.2mm (3in) gun.

KV-1A

Powerplant:	410kW (550hp) V-2K V-12 diesel engine
Performance:	The KV-1A had a maximum road speed of 35km/h (22mph) and a road range of 250km (155 miles)
Dimensions:	Length: 6.25m (20ft 6in); width 3.25m (10ft 9in); height 2.75m (9ft)

Despite its heavy armour the early KV-1 was vulnerable at close range.

sent to the Finnish front for evaluation and were approved. Named the KV-1 to honour Klementy Voroshilov, a Marshal of the Soviet Union and pre-war defence commissar, it went into full-scale production. Some 141 examples of the KV-1A were built in 1940, and a further 211 before the German invasion on 22 June 1941. Thus reasonable numbers of this fine tank were available to be rushed to the front line. The KV-1s, with their 'shell-proof' armour, shocked the Germans, but this advantage was neutralized by its poorly trained crews, who too often moved too close instead of picking off the enemy from a safe range.

Later a heavy new cast turret was added, slowing the KV-1 down. This prompted one general to ask Stalin what was the point of this unmanoeuvrable tank that broke bridges but had only the armament of a medium tank.

SOVIET UNION

KV-2

The grotesque KV-2 was built to meet the need for a heavy tank to assault fixed emplacements. Although effective in this task, its great weight and size proved its downfall. Only 330 were built before production was discontinued at the end of 1941.

Later models were designated KV-2B and had a larger mantlet with rounded shield. Some had flamethrowers. Built on the KV-1A chassis, they were 4 tonnes (3.6 tons) heavier.

The KV-2 had a crew of six: commander, gunner, loader, auxiliary driver, driver-mechanic and radio-operator.

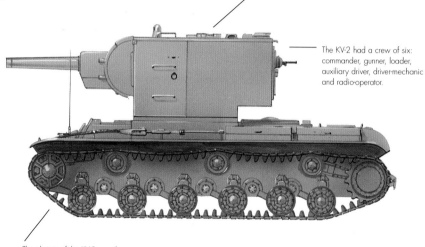

The chassis of the KV-2 was the same as the KV-1, but the latter was 10 tonnes (9.8 tons) heavier.

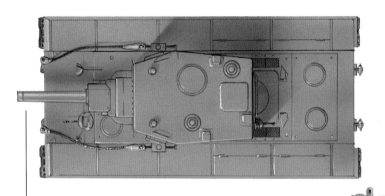

The heaviest armour was 110mm (4.3in) thick on the front face of the turret.

The KV-2's gun could penetrate 72mm (2.8in) of armour at 1500m (4920ft). A special concrete-piercing shell was developed for attacking fortifications.

The 152mm (5.9in) gun was the largest calibre weapon mounted on an Allied tank during the war, although later Soviet tanks had more powerful long-barrelled guns.

The KV-2's greater weight on the same chassis as the KV-I caused much poorer mechanical reliability, and many broke down.

SOVIET UNION

261

W hen the KV (Klementy Voroshilov) tank was put into production in 1940, it appeared in two forms – the KV-1 battle tank with a 76.2mm (3in) gun and the 'artillery tank' version with a huge slab-sided turret and a massive 152mm (5.9in) howitzer. Fighting against the Mannerheim Line in Finland had shown the need for a 'bunker buster' to

The Germans captured many KV-2s and put them into their own service.

destroy fixed fortifications. The KV-2 was developed quickly and prototypes with a 122mm (4.8in) gun went into action on a combat trial at the Mannerheim Line in early 1940. In late 1940, the KV-2 was accepted for production with a 152mm (5.9in) gun.

The KV-2 outgunned everything it met, and with thicker armour than most tanks of the war it was virtually indestructible. However, the tracks were a weak point and German gunners learned to target these to disable the KV-2s. With a weight of around 52 tonnes (51.1tons), the KV-2 was slow and cumbersome. The turret was so tall that it was easy to see and hit from a distance. If the tank was on an incline, the turret was almost impossible to turn.

KV-2

Powerplant:	410kW (550hp) V-2K V-12 diesel engine
Performance:	The KV-2 had a maximum road speed of 26km/h (16mph) and a road range of 140km (87 miles)
Dimensions:	length: 6.79m (22ft 3in); width: 3.32m (10ft 11in); height: 3.65m (12ft)

Many KV-2s were captured by German forces and then put into service as the Sturmpanzer KW II(r). The Germans converted KV-2s for their own use by adding their own lighting system and a commander's cupola. They planned to use some as assault tanks in the invasion of Malta, but this never took place.

This KV-2 was abandoned in a defensive position.

SOVIET UNION

263

T-34/76A

The T-34 was probably the most important tank of the war. It was easy to build and simple to operate and became available in its many thousands. The T34/76 models with the 76.2mm (3in) gun had several faults and each major production block featured new improvements.

The original two-man turret was so cramped that the commander had to aim and fire the main gun. Both he and the loader had to share one hatch.

The early T-34s had no commander's cupola and no direct vision devices, which forced him to expose himself to fire when looking around.

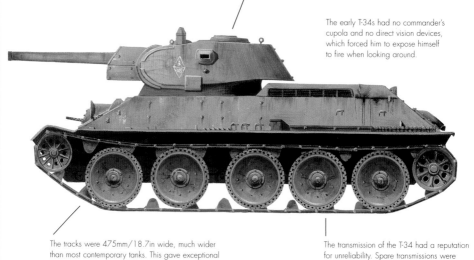

The tracks were 475mm/18.7in wide, much wider than most contemporary tanks. This gave exceptional cross-country manoeuvrability.

The transmission of the T-34 had a reputation for unreliability. Spare transmissions were often carried on the rear deck of the tank.

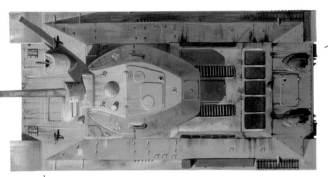

The T-34's water-cooled diesel engine was taken from the last of the BT tanks, the BT-8.

The base of the turret under the gun mantlet was a notorious 'shot trap', concentrating the effect of a shell hit at a vulnerable area, blowing the turret off.

T-34/76 models of 1940 used the L-11 Model 1938 76.2mm (3in) rifled gun, but on the Model 1941, the much better F-34 cannon was fitted. This had greater range and hitting power than the guns on the contemporary Panzer III and IV.

The T-34 was the first tank to make extensive use of sloped armour for ballistic protection. Sloping the glacis plate at 60 degrees gave the 45mm (1.77in) armour the effective thickness of 75mm (2.95in).

SOVIET UNION

The T-34 was built in quantities barely equalled by any other AFV and, while not perfect, had perhaps the best fighting qualities of any tank of the war.

Remarkably, the Soviets managed to keep its existence completely secret until the German invasion in June 1941. Developed by the experimental department of the Kharkov Locomotive Factory as the T-32, it was followed by the T-34, which had thicker armour as well as other improvements.

In early 1940, two prototypes of the T-34 were put through gruelling trials and demonstrated in the Kremlin courtyard, where they found favour with the Soviet leadership, which soon ordered 220, then 600 units.

The Germans were shocked to encounter the T-34 in June 1941, having believed that all Soviet tanks were either lightweights or lumbering, multi-turreted monsters. The T-34 was fast, well armed and highly manoeuvrable, and its armour was sloped to maximum protection. German anti-tank shells just bounced off, unless they struck under the gun mantlet, which was unfortunately a 'shot trap'.

The gun of the original model, the T34/76A, was a dual-purpose weapon that could fire high explosive and armour-

With excellent mobility, firepower and armour, the T-34/76 was the best tank in the world in 1941/42.

T-34/76A

Powerplant:	373kW (500hp) V-2-34 V-12 diesel engine
Performance:	The T-34/76A had a maximum road speed of 55km/h (34mph) and a road range of 300km (186 miles)
Dimensions:	length: 5.92m (19ft 5in); width: 3m (9ft 7in); height: 2.45m (8ft 1in)

The T-34 demonstrated the advantages of sloped armour in deflecting armour-piercing shells fired at its front and sides.

piercing shells and was fitted in a cramped two-man rolled/pressed steel turret.

The T-34's sloped armour and wide tracks influenced tank design worldwide. The T-34 forced the Germans to counter it and inspired the design of the Panther.

SOVIET UNION

T-34/85

Possibly the best tank of the war, the T-34/85 was fast, manoeuvrable and hard-hitting. Appearing in huge numbers from early 1944, it led the assault on Germany until the end of the war, when it was widely exported to many communist nations. Total production of all T-34 models was over 64,000.

The T-34/85 introduced a commander's cupola with vision blocks. This allowed him to view the outside without being exposed to fire.

The auxiliary diesel tanks could be jettisoned in combat to prevent fire. Variations of this feature were found on many post-war Soviet tanks.

The Christie suspension of earlier Soviet tanks was retained. Each wheel was fitted to its own long forward-angled spring unit inside the hull.

A new five-speed gearbox improved the drivability of the T-34/85 compared to earlier models.

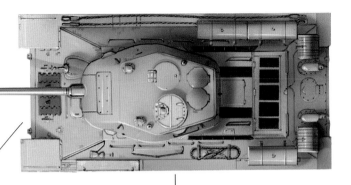

Armour thickness on the glacis plate was increased to 75mm (2.95in). This was not thick by contemporary standards, but the sloping increased its effectiveness.

The T-34/85 had dual turret hatches fitted as standard, greatly improving the crew's survival chances if the tank was hit.

The driver sat in the front left hull and used periscopes to see when the hatch was closed. Next to him was the radio operator, who also fired the 7.62mm (0.3in) DT bow machine gun.

The major change in T-34 production after 1943 was the arrival of the 85mm (3.34in) gun T-34/85, which had a new three-man turret and a larger-diameter turret ring. Both the T-34/76 and /85 were built in parallel until mid-1944, when production of the former stopped after 35,099 had been completed.

The huge losses of T-34s in 1941 and 1943 were due respectively to the speed and

Red Army T34/85s pass German prisoners in the final months of the war.

surprise of the German advance and the development of new German heavy tanks, such as the Tiger and Panther. The Panther, in particular, was designed with sloped armour modelled after the T-34 and with a long-barrelled 75mm (2.95in) gun that matched the Soviet 76.2mm (3in) gun. Although

T-34/85

Powerplant:	373kW (500hp) V-2-34 V-12 diesel engine
Performance:	The T-34/85 had a maximum road speed of 55km/h (34mph) and a road range of 300km (186 miles)
Dimensions:	Length: 8.15m (26ft 7in); width: 3m (9ft 10in); height: 2.74 m (9ft)

Soviet and Polish soldiers enter Berlin aboard a T-34/85, 1945.

similar in appearance and using the same automotive components, the T-34/85 was a major redesign, with a new three-man turret, the same as that used on the KV-85. The new gun was the D-5T85 (later replaced by the ZIS-S53) dual-purpose 85mm (3.34in) gun, which could fire shells able to penetrate 102mm (4in) of armour at 1000m (3280ft). This was enough to defeat a Panther or Tiger at closer range.

The T-34/85 was rolling off the production lines in January 1944, only five months after the design was initiated. That year over 11,000 were produced and these played the major role in pushing the Germans back into Germany in late 1944. The T-34/85 remained the principal Soviet tank until the late 1940s.

T-60

Some time after other nations had abandoned light tank development, the Soviet Army was still persisting with two-man mini tanks like the T-60. Little better than the T-40 from which it was derived, it was nevertheless built in large numbers.

The T-60 had a two-man crew, consisting of a driver and a commander/gunner.

Although cast turrets had been developed in the Soviet Union, the T-60 had a welded unit for simplicity of manufacture.

The main armament was only a 20mm (0.78in) ShVAK cannon, which was adequate against troops and light armour, but useless if the T-60 encountered enemy medium tanks.

The late model versions were designated the T-60A and had increased armour. They also had solid road wheels rather than the spoked wheels of the T-60.

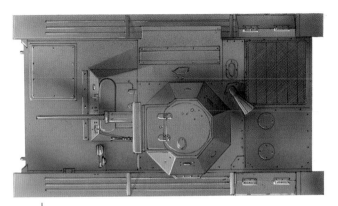

The ShVAK cannon, which later became a very widely used Soviet weapon, was developed for the T-60. It could fire armour-piercing shells.

The T-60's turret was offset to the left side and the engine was beside it on the right. The driver sat in the centre at the front.

Surplus T-60s were converted to a number of uses. Some became mounts for Katyusha rocket launchers. Others were employed as tractors to tow 57mm (2.24in) artillery guns.

SOVIET UNION

In 1939, the Soviets introduced the two-man T-40 light amphibious tank. This was issued mainly to reconnaissance units, which used its amphibious capability mainly for river crossings. Unfortunately, its armour

The low-powered T-60 was too slow to scout ahead of the battle tanks.

was no more than 14mm (0.5in) thick, which was inadequate. The perceived need for a light cavalry tank saw the T-40 redesigned without amphibious capability as the T-60, which appeared in November 1941. The armour thickness was increased to up to 25mm (0.98in), but the main weapon remained only a 20mm (0.78in) cannon. The low-powered engine made it little faster than the medium tanks for which it was scouting. Nonetheless, the T-60 was reliable, even in winter, its low footprint letting it cross soft ground, snow and ice where a heavier tank could not. Over 6000 were produced, the last models having increased armour.

T-60A

Powerplant:	63kW (85hp) GAZ-203 six-cylinder petrol engine
Performance:	The T-60 had a maximum road speed of 44km/h (27 mph) and a road range of 450km (279 miles)
Dimensions:	length: 4.8m (13ft 6in); width: 2.3m (7ft 8in); height: 1.74m (5ft 8in)

The T-60 was used for the one of the most unusual experiments in the history of armoured vehicles – the Kyrliati Tank (KT), or winged tank. This involved fitting a set of wooden biplane wings and a tail to allow the T-60 to glide to the battlefront. It was successful in trials, but a lack of suitable towing aircraft ended the project in 1942.

The T-60 was light and simple and was produced in large numbers.

T-70

Built as a replacement for the obsolete T-60, the T-70 was better all round but still no match against heavy weapons. Cheap and fast to produce, thousands were issued until Soviet medium tank production could recover from the onslaught of summer 1941.

Like most early war Soviet tanks, the T-70 had no cupola for the commander. The forward-hinged turret hatch was his only protection when commanding the tank from outside.

Some T-70s were built as mounts for the SU-37 anti-aircraft gun.

Armament stowage increased from 70 to 94 rounds on later models.

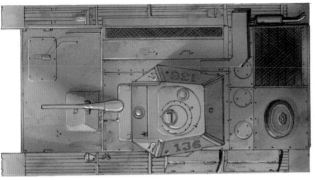

The T-70A had a revised model of the twin truck engines of the T-70. The new GAZ-203 gave 63kW (85hp) versus the 52kW (70hp) GAZ-202.

Most T-70s were built with the 45mm (1.77in) 1938 gun as the main weapon. The commander also fired the 7.62mm (0.3in) DT coaxial machine gun.

The heaviest armour on the T-70A was on the turret front at 60mm (2.36in). This was increased from 35mm (1.37in) on the T-70.

T-70s appearing from September 1942 had strengthened running gear, tracks widened to 300mm (11.8in), wider road wheels and return rollers. The drive wheels and driveshafts were improved.

SOVIET UNION

Despite the obsolescence of the two-man light tanks, the disruption caused by the German invasion meant that such vehicles were all that could be produced in any numbers. The T-60 tank was under-armed, poorly armoured and underpowered.

Although similar in concept and appearance to the T-60, the T-70 was a complete redesign. The lack of power of the T-60 was addressed by adopting a layout of

The T-70 was a less-than-successful redesign of the obsolete T-60.

T-70

Powerplant:	twin 52kW (70hp) GAZ-202 six-cylinder petrol engine
Performance:	The T-70 had a maximum road speed of 51km/h (32mph) and a road range of 450km (279 miles)
Dimensions:	length: 4.28m (14ft 11in); width: 2.42m (7ft 11in); height: 2.03m (6ft 8in)

Large numbers of T-70s were built, although they were outmoded by 1943.

two truck engines, connected to the front drive wheels by a single shaft. A new turret housed a 45mm (1.7in) gun, but its commander still had the problem of having to load and fire the gun as well as direct the tank.

The T-70 arrived on the front lines at the end of January 1942 and began to replace the T-60. The twin engine layout proved too complex and underwent revision. In general, however, the T-70 was fast and manoeuvrable and could climb gradients of up to 70 per cent. The T-70A was a revised version that had heavier armour and a more angular turret with a squared-off rear face. It entered production during 1943. Production of the T-70 series ended in October 1943 with a total output of 8226. By this time, medium tank production had recovered in the new factories east of the Ural mountains.

SOVIET UNION

KV-85

Designed to counter the new generation of German tanks – the Tiger and Panther – the KV-85 turned out to be inferior and only 130 were produced, all in 1943. It was the last tank in the KV series, but served as the basis of several self-propelled assault guns.

The KV-85 introduced a commander's cupola with a ring of vision slots. Like the majority of Soviet tanks, the KV-85 did not have a machine gun for anti-aircraft defence.

A rotating periscope was fitted ahead of the cupola to give the commander a view without opening his hatch.

Early models of the KV-85 had a five-man crew, but during production the bow gun was deleted and the radio equipment relocated to the turret.

The KV-85 had a new cast steel turret designed for the IS-1, the first of the 'Stalin' tanks. It was later adapted for use on the T-34/85.

The KV-85 was armed with an 85mm (3.34in) D-5T cannon and two 7.6mm (0.3in) DT machine guns.

The new turret required a bigger turret ring and modifications to the upper hull, which included triangular fillets along the track guards.

The use of thinner armour made the KV-85 slightly lighter than the KV-1A.

SOVIET UNION

The KV-85's designation hints at its origin, as a development of the KV-1 heavy tank with an 85mm (3.34in) gun. The last KV-1 model, the KV-1S, which retained a 76.2mm (3in) gun, had many improvements over its predecessors and most of these were incorporated in the KV-85. Going against all trends of tank development, the KV-1S and KV-85 had less

The KV-85 was a lighter, faster version of the KV-1.

armour than earlier models (down from 130mm/5.1in to 60mm/2.36in on the hull sides, for example), but this gave it 25 per cent greater speed and better mobility. The same V-12 448kW (600hp) diesel engine now gave a 9.7kW (13.1hp) per ton power-to-weight ratio. An entirely new cast steel turret of the type designed for the IS-1 was fitted and this featured a commander's cupola for the first time on a KV-series tank. The rear-facing machine gun was eliminated and the crew was reduced from five to four, comprising a commander, a driver, a loader/mechanic and a gunner.

Production began in the autumn of 1943 and the 27th Independent Guard Tank Penetration Regiment took the KV-85 into action in early December, when it suffered

KV-85

Powerplant:	448kW (600hp) V-2 V-12 diesel engine
Performance:	The KV-85 had a maximum road speed of 42km/h (26mph) and a road range of 330km (205 miles)
Dimensions:	length: 8.6m (28ft 2in); width: 3.25m (10ft 9in); height: 2.8m (9ft 2in)

heavy losses. The KV-85 was designed to counter the increasing number of Tigers on the battlefield, but the Tiger had the bigger gun, the thicker armour and, usually, the greater numbers, so it won most encounters on the open steppes of western Russia and the Ukraine.

The KV-85's best features, its new turret and 85mm gun, were adopted for use on late-model T-34s.

IS-2 (IOSEF STALIN)

*The Iosef Stalin 2 heavy tank was the most
powerfully armed main battle tank of the war.
Over 2000 were built. It was developed into the
IS-3 with a new rounded turret, and this
became the model for all post-war Soviet tanks.*

During 1944, provision was made for
a DShK machine gun on the cupola for
anti-aircraft defence.

The two-part 122mm
(4.8in) shells were so
large that only 28
rounds could be
carried inside the IS-2.

The massive 122mm (4.8in) A-19
Corps artillery gun could shoot a
shell completely through a Panther
from front to back from a distance
of 1500m (4920ft).

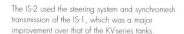

The IS-2 used the steering system and synchromesh
transmission of the IS-1, which was a major
improvement over that of the KV-series tanks.

One disadvantage of the 122mm (4.8in) gun, which itself weighed nearly 2 tonnes (1.9 tons), was that the shell and cartridge were separate and had to be combined before firing. This restricted the rate of fire to three rounds per minute at best.

Auxiliary fuel tanks could be carried at the rear of the IS-2. These tanks could be jettisoned if necessary.

Later model IS-2s had a redesigned bow, which provided better ballistic protection and allowed for a 12mm (0.47in) gun.

SOVIET UNION

The Iosef Stalin 2 combined the best features of the KV-series tanks with the firepower of a naval destroyer. It shared with the IS-1 an improved gearbox and better distribution of armour. The main difference was the 122mm (4.8in) D-25T gun, which fired a projectile with over three times the kinetic energy of the 76.2mm (3in) round, the heaviest in service in 1941.

Even if it failed to penetrate the armour of a German Panther or Tiger, the explosive charge in the 25kg (55lb) shell was often enough to blow the turret off its mount. Both 100mm (3.9in) and 122mm (4.8in) guns had been proposed for the IS-2, the

A column of IS-2s lead the Soviet assault on Berlin in April 1945.

IS-2 (Iosef Stalin)

Powerplant:	382.8kW (513hp) V-2-IS V-12 diesel engine
Performance:	The IS-2 had a maximum road speed of 37km/h (23mph) and a road range of 240km (150 miles)
Dimensions:	length: 9.83m (32ft 3in); width: 3.07m (10ft); height: 2.73m (8ft 11in)

The IS-2 was superior to the German Tiger in most respects.

former proving superior in trials, but it was easier to mass-produce the 122 and its ammunition and this was officially chosen in December 1943.

The first IS-2s saw combat in February 1944. Of all the weapons at that time, only the 88mm (3.46in) gun of the Tiger I had any chance of penetrating the 160mm (6.29in) frontal armour at long range. The IS-2 could defeat a Panther at 1500m (4920ft), while the Panther had to get as close as 400m (1310ft). Many IS-1s were rebuilt with the new gun and both types led the Soviet advance on Berlin. About 2500 IS-2s were built before the IS-3 replaced it in production in early 1945. Some were rebuilt as armoured recovery vehicles, being the only machines able to recover damaged IS-2s on the battlefield.

SOVIET UNION

BM-13 KATYUSHA

The Katyusha, or 'Little Katy', rocket system was a simple but extremely effective form of artillery, able to bring a heavy weight of fire on enemy position ahead of a ground assault. Versions of the Katyusha are still used today in many parts of the world.

The rocket used on early Katyushas was the 132mm (5in) M-13, a lengthened version of the RS-132 aircraft rocket. The M-13 had stabilizing fins, mainly to speed production compared to more complex spin-stabilized rockets favoured by other nations.

The name Katyusha, came from a popular song that was a favourite with soldiers.

This Katyusha is mounted on an American Studebaker truck chassis. Over 100,000 of these vehicles were supplied to the Soviet Union, where they were designated the U3.

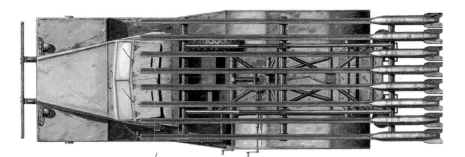

Various sizes of rocket rack were manufactured. The version illustrated mounts eight rails with rockets fitted to both the top and bottom of each rail.

Later rockets on the Katyusha included the M-20 with less fuel and more explosive. Rockets of up to 203mm (7.9in) calibre were trialled during the war.

The front windscreen panels of the truck was covered with armoured shutters to protect the cab from the serious back-blast of flames and debris.

The Katyusha was widely exported after the war, particularly to Middle Eastern nations and to Asia, where they saw action in the Korean and Vietnam wars.

SOVIET UNION

289

SOVIET UNION

The famous 'Katyusha' Soviet artillery rocket system was developed in secret before the war and rushed into action to counter the German invasion in June 1941. The Katyusha (Little Katy) was a generic name for an array of rocket rails that could be fitted on a truck chassis or even on obsolete light tanks, coastal watercraft and armoured trains. It was usually mounted on the Russian ZIS-6 truck or the American Studebaker 6x6, large numbers of which were supplied from 1942. The Katyusha used adapted aircraft air-to-ground rockets with fragmentation warheads.

The Katyusha system could be used in many ways. Here, ground-based launchers fire at Stalingrad in 1943.

When the invasion came, the first battery of seven launch trucks (designated BM-13-16) and 600 rockets was rushed to Smolensk. So effective were they that mass production of launchers, rockets and parts began in nearly 200 factories. By the war's end, over 10,000 launchers and 12 million rockets had been produced, and 500 Soviet Guards Mortar batteries were equipped with the Katyusha.

BM-13 Katyusha

Powerplant:	64kW (86hp) Hercules JXD six-cylinder petrol engine
Performance:	The Katyusha had a maximum road speed of approximately 69km/h (43mph) and road range of 402km (250 miles)
Dimensions:	length: 6.33m (20ft 9in); width: 2.23m (7ft 9in); height: 2.7m (8ft 10in)

It was most effective used en masse before an assault. The falling rockets delivered a lot of explosives in a short time and their screaming demoralized enemy forces for a wide radius around the target. Katyushas on newer truck bodies remained in service into the 1980s and were widely exported.

A Russian soldier loads a truck-mounted BM-13 launcher in 1945.

SOVIET UNION

SU-76

*The SU-76 was a Samokhodnaya Ustanovka
(self-propelled mounting) based on the
T-70 tank. It was built in huge numbers and
was distributed to many Soviet 'client states'
after the war. They could be found in some
armies up to the 1980s.*

The SU-76 was armed with a
76.2mm (3in) ZIS-3 cannon.
Most also had secondary
armament of one 7.62mm
(0.3in) DT machine gun.

The engines were
mounted at the front of
the vehicle, with one
driving each track.

The chassis was that of the T-70 tank, but
lengthened and with an extra road wheel
each side to handle the increased weight.

The Germans were astonished in early 1944 to find a version called the SU-76i, which had the same superstructure and armament as the M, but which was mounted on captured Panzer III chassis. It was twice as heavy, and over 200 were converted.

The lack of protection or creature comforts (the driver sat directly next to the throbbing engines) led to the nickname 'Sukami' (bitch) for these early SU vehicles.

The SU-76 was a relatively small low profile vehicle with a combat weight of only 11.2 tonnes (11 tons).

The improved Su-76M of 1943 relocated the engines to an inline arrangement and had a number of detail changes to the hull.

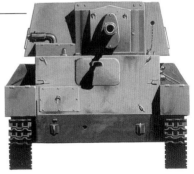

SOVIET UNION

293

SOVIET UNION

By 1945, some 12,661 of the SU-76 'Light Mechanized Gun' had been built, second only in numbers to the T-34. The original version, produced from December 1942, had separate engines for each track and the main gun exactly on the centreline. On later models, this was shifted to the left, letting the engine compartment

Despite its many faults, the SU-76 was built in very large quantities.

be placed on the right, with one engine behind the other and a single gearbox. The obsolete T-70 tank, on which the SU-76 was based, had this arrangement, proving the old adage, 'If it ain't broke, don't fix it!'

The SU-76M was the main production version, first appearing in May 1943. Lightly armoured, it had only 35mm (1.37in) of armour on the upper hull and no overhead covering other than a tarpaulin for the gun crew. The gun could traverse 32 degrees within its mount. The ZIS-3 'divisional gun' fired 12 rounds per minute and was a proven artillery piece and anti-tank gun, making it

SU-76M

Powerplant:	Twin 63kW (85hp) GAZ-203 six-cylinder petrol engines
Performance:	The Su-76 had a maximum speed of 45km/h (28mph) and a road range of 320km (198 miles)
Dimensions:	length: 4.88m (16ft 9in); width: 2.74m (9ft); height: 2.17m (7ft 1in)

the obvious choice for a Samokhodnaya Ustanovka (self-propelled mounting). By the time the SU-76 was available in numbers, though, this gun could easily be outranged by most German anti-tank guns. Newer assault guns were available, and the SU-76s were relegated to indirect fire-support roles.

An American soldier examines an SU-76 captured from North Korean forces in 1950.

SOVIET UNION

SU-152

The SU-152 was fitted with the largest gun mounted on a production AFV during World War II. It was rushed into development in the first months of 1943 and performed well at the Battle of Kursk in July. It was followed by the similar ISU-152, based on the IS-3 chassis.

The SU-152 had no fixed secondary armament, but sometimes mounted a DShK machine gun for anti-aircraft protection.

One of the best features of the SU-152 was its low profile, which helped it use ambush tactics against German armour. It received the nickname Zveroboy ('animal hunter').

Production of the SU-152 amounted to 704 before production switched to the ISU-152 based on the IS-3.

The SU-152 was based on the chassis of the proven KV-1S tank, which greatly eased maintenance.

The SU-152 mounted the huge 152mm (5.9in) Model 1937 gun, firing extremely powerful high explosive shells. The ISU-152's ML-20S version of the gun could also fire armour-piercing shells, although it had a lower muzzle velocity.

A penalty of the compact superstructure was the cramped interior, and as few as 20 rounds and their cartridges could be carried internally. This meant that the 152s either needed an entourage of ammunition carriers or had to stay close to field howitzer positions if they were to have any combat persistence.

German success with heavy assault guns used in the anti-tank role caused Soviet tank designers to evaluate this type of vehicle in 1942. The team behind the KV-1 heavy tank adapted several examples with new casemate hulls and 76.2mm (3in) guns. One of these, the KV-7, had two guns mounted in parallel,

The SU-152 was an immensely powerful self-propelled gun.

which looked impressive but had little effect on hitting power. The new hull design was adopted, however, for the carriage of a massive 152mm (5.9in) 'corps howitzer-cannon'. This gun was a field artillery piece designed for both long range artillery support (indirect fire) and direct assault on fortifications. When mounted in the new vehicle, which was accepted as the SU-152 in early 1943, it could fire a 52kg (115lb) high-explosive shell over 5000m (16,404ft) and a lighter anti-tank shell the same distance with less elevation. Like other Soviet AFVs, the SU-152 was often the carriage for 'tank descent squads', platoons of infantry hitching a lift into battle, and incidentally providing some protection.

The SU-152 debuted at Kursk in July 1943, leading the counterattack alongside the medium tanks and playing an important part in the Soviet victory. The SU-152 and its successor, based on the IS-2 and designated ISU-152, blasted their way through fortifications and armour all the way to Berlin.

A squad of SU-152s cross a river in Latvia during the 1944 Soviet offensive.

SU-152

Powerplant:	382.8kW (513kW) V-2-K V-12 diesel engine
Performance:	The SU-152 had a maximum road speed of 43km/h (27mph) and a road range of 320km (198 miles)
Dimensions:	length: 8.95m (29ft 4in); width: 3.25m (10ft 9in); height: 2.45m (8ft 1in)

SOVIET UNION

CHAR B1 BIS

The Char B1 was the main tank in French service in 1940. Despite its good features, such as heavy armament and thick armour, they were poorly employed and wasted in small-scale actions rather than being concentrated in force.

The Germans took the turrets off many of the Char B1s they captured and turned them into flamethrower tanks for garrison duties.

The first Char B1s had a 37mm (1.46in) turret gun, quickly replaced by a 47mm (1.85in) weapon.

Maximum range could only be achieved in low gear at a painful 10–11km/h (6–7mph).

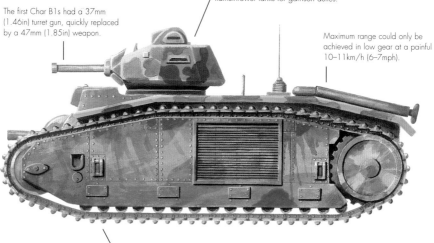

The driver aimed the main gun by positioning the tank, with the help of an ingenious hydrostatic gearbox. He elevated it if necessary, and then fired.

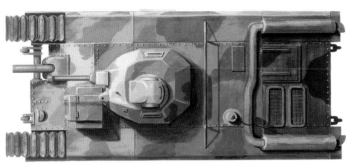

The commander in the one-man turret was overloaded, directing the driver and loading and firing the 47mm (1.85in) gun.

Despite its protracted development and outdated concept, the Char B1 had heavier armour (up to 60mm/ 2.36in) thick) and heavier armament than the majority of tanks outside the Soviet Union at the beginning of the war.

The bis was the second production variant, identified by a longer turret gun. Three-quarters of the 400 Char B1s built were this model.

A few late models, designated Char B-ter had a hull gun with a limited traverse.

FRANCE

In the latter part of World War I, the French developed some of the first truly practical tanks. However, they failed to capitalize on their lead in tank design, believing that the next war would be fought along the same lines as the last. The Char (tank) B1 bis (improved) was a case in point, designed with a long track that circled

Poor tactics prevented the Char B1 being used effectively in 1940.

the hull sides for the greatest ground contact and thus trench-crossing ability. The specification for a heavy tank was issued as early as 1921, but it was five years before this was agreed in final form and another nine before Renault's winning design was put into production as the Char B1.

The hull-mounted 75mm (2.95in) gun was intended as a close-support weapon (the turret was meant for dealing with enemy tanks). The whole tank had to be aimed to use it. In a head-on encounter this might have worked, but both the faster German tanks and the long-range anti-tank guns scored hits on the thin side armour before the Char B1 could align itself.

Char B1 bis

Powerplant:	223.8kW (300hp) Renault six-cylinder petrol engine
Performance:	The Char B1bis had a maximum road speed of 28km/h (17.4mph) and a road range of 160km (100 miles)
Dimensions:	length: 6.37m (20ft 11in); width: 2.5m (8ft 2in); height: 2.79m (9ft 2in)

Each of the four French armoured divisions created by May 1940 had two battalions, each including 35 Char B1s. In battle these soon fell into disarray and the surviving Char B1s were carted off to become driver training tanks for the German army.

Many French tanks, like this Char B1, were named after France's regions or overseas colonies.

FRANCE

303

HOTCHKISS H-35

*Like the similar Renault R.35, the Hotchkiss
H-35 was available in large numbers at the time
of the German Blitzkrieg. The H-35 suffered
from its poor gun and one-man turret, but its
thick cast armour encouraged the Germans to
develop more effective anti-tank guns.*

There was no turret floor and the commander
sat on a saddle that was suspended and
moved with the turret.

The short-barrelled
1918-model 37mm
(1.46in) gun was
ineffective against
most German armour.
The rate of fire was
low because the
commander had to
load and fire it
himself.

The commander had a rear door on the
turret, which could be folded down to form
a seat. Otherwise he used a rotating
cupola for vision.

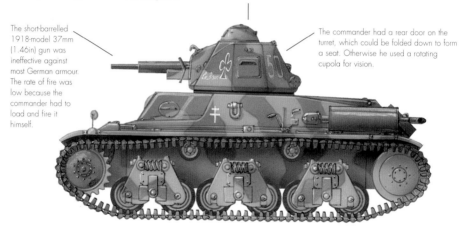

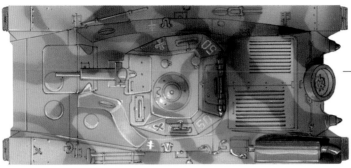

The engine was at the rear left and the fuel tank on the right. An external fuel tank could also be used.

The driver's position was in the front, offset slightly to the right. He had a two-part split hatch cover. There was an escape hatch in the floor to form a seat.

The H-35's hull was made of cast sections bolted together. The turret was fully cast.

The Germans added radios to their captured H-35s and converted some to self-propelled artillery with 75mm (2.95in) anti-tank guns or 105mm (4.1in) howitzers.

FRANCE

305

FRANCE

The French army ordered a new light tank in 1933 to complement the SOMUA S-35s in the mechanized infantry divisions. It rejected Hotchkiss's prototype in favour of a similar Renault design, but the cavalry produced it as the H-35. The turret was the same as the S-35 and contained a short-barrelled 1918-model 37mm (1.46in) gun. After modifications, the H-35 was adopted by the army for the infantry support role.

In production the engine was upgraded from one of 56kW (75hp) to one of 90kW

H-39s pass in review at a pre-war French military parade.

Hotchkiss H-35

Powerplant:	56kW (75hp) Hotchkiss 1935 six-cylinder petrol engine
Performance:	The H-35 had a maximum road speed of 27km/h (17mph) and a road range of 150km (93 miles)
Dimensions:	length: 4.22m (13ft 10in); width: 1.95m (6ft 5in); height: 2.15m (7ft 1in)

The H-35 was well armoured but insufficiently armed and had little effect in stemming the German Blitzkrieg in May/June 1940.

(120hp), which increased the top speed only slightly. This model, known as the H-39, had a higher top deck, while later examples had a long-barrelled 37mm (1.46in) gun. Only platoon commanders were equipped with the long gun version by May 1940.

During the Battle of France, the slow pace of the H-35s and their weak gun left them unable to slow the German advance. However, the heavy armour saved many from destruction and these were captured, to be used mainly as gun tugs or driver training vehicles. They did equip some German units for garrison duties in Yugoslavia. Vichy French forces also retained their H-35s. Surplus H-35 turrets were installed as fixed emplacements on the Atlantic wall defences.

FRANCE

SOMUA S-35

*The best French tank in 1940, the SOMUA S-35
had good armour, armament and performance.
The speed of the German advance, however,
and the use of air power prevented any tanks
mounting an effective defence. Many of
the surviving S-35s entered service with
German units.*

The S-35 had the same
turret as the Char B1 bis
heavy tank.

The door on the left side of the
hull was the main exit, but there
was also an escape hatch in the
underside.

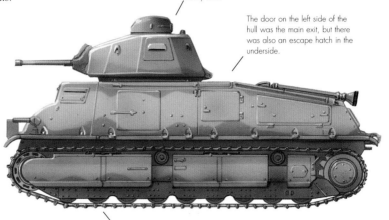

There were 18 road wheels, protected by
armoured skirts that could be hinged
upwards for maintenance.

The engine was positioned at the left rear with a self-sealing gas tank on the right. There was a fireproof bulkhead separating the fighting compartment from the engine.

The 47mm (1.85in) SA 35 high-velocity gun could fire high explosive and armour-piercing shells.

The S-35 had the same type of one-man turret used on other French tanks, although on the S-35 it was electrically traversed, which reduced the commander's burden.

The cast hull was constructed of upper and lower halves joined by bolts. If hit here by an anti-tank shell, the tank could split and fall apart.

FRANCE

FRANCE

One feature of the SOMUA S-35 was a powered turret.

Intended for use by mechanized cavalry units, the SOMUA (Société d'Outillage Mécanique et d'Usinage d'Artillerie) S-35 medium tank appeared in 1935. It was the first tank to appear with both a cast hull and a cast turret, although the hull was constructed in sections and bolted together.

In many ways it was one of the best tanks of the early war period, having armour and armament comparable to the Panzer IV. Deliveries began in 1936, and about 500 had been completed by May 1940, but only half were in service with combat units. All were supposed to have radios, but only about 20 per cent did due to shortages. On one of the few occasions when a significant number were able to concentrate for an attack against the advancing Germans, they were wiped out by Stuka dive-bombers.

Like other French tanks of the period, the S-35 featured a cramped one-man turret, preventing the commander from doing his job effectively. Visibility for the crew was

Despite its resemblance to other French tanks of 1940, the SOMUA S-35 was more effective than its contemporaries.

SOMUA S-35

Powerplant:	142kW (190hp) SOMUA V-8r petrol engine
Performance:	The S-35 had a maximum road speed of 41km/h (25 mph) and a road range of 230km (143 miles)
Dimensions:	length: 5.38m (17ft 8in); width: 2.12m (6ft 11in); height: 2.62m (8ft 7in)

poor and access to the engine for maintenance was difficult.

An improved model, the S-40, was under evaluation with a 164kW (220hp) engine and improved suspension, but only a few were completed by the time of the French capitulation. Similarly, only a prototype of the SAU-40 self-propelled gun was completed. Several hundred were passed on to Italy, and

the S-35 had a second lease of life later in the war, when a shortage of tanks led the Germans to withdraw many examples from storage and issued them to training units.

Free French units used the S-35 in the North African campaign and others were recaptured after the Normandy invasion and used by French units. Despite their age, some of these tanks were used well into the post-war era, making the S-35 one of the longest lived tanks developed in the 1930s.

FRANCE

GLOSSARY

AFV Armoured Fighting Vehicle. Generic term for any armed and armoured military vehicle.

AP Armour Piercing. Ammunition designed to penetrate and destroy armoured vehicles. AP shells usually have non-explosive solid warheads.

APC Armoured Personnel Carrier. Armour-protected transport vehicle for troops.

Armoured car Wheeled vehicle with armour protection. Can be lightly or heavily armed.

Ausf Ausführung. German for 'Model', as in Ausf A, Ausf G, etc.

AVRE Armoured Vehicle Royal Engineers. A British term for a combat engineering vehicle.

Barbette A fixed (non-rotating) gun housing. The gun itself may have elevation and limited traverse.

Blindé French for 'Armoured'.

Blitzkrieg German term meaning 'lightning war'. A fast-paced strategy combining armour, motorized infantry and airpower all linked by radio to exploit weaknesses in enemy defences. Also refers to the campaigns in 1939–41 in which it was used effectively.

BT Bystrokhodny Tank. Soviet term for a class of fast tank larger than a light tank but smaller than a medium tank.

Calibre Internal diameter of a gun or cannon.

Calibres Length of a gun expressed as a multiple of its internal diameter.

Cannon Small-calibre gun firing explosive shells or a large-calibre main gun firing AP, HE or other types of shell.

Carro Armato Italian for 'armoured vehicle'.

Char French for tank, literally 'chariot'.

Coaxial Two or more guns in the same turret or barbette firing in the same axis.

Cupola Armour-plated revolving position on top of AFV turret to give commander better view and protection.

Depression Angle by which a gun can point below the horizontal.

Elevation Angle by which a gun can point above the horizontal. Broadly speaking, the higher the elevation, the longer the range.

Feldhaubitze German for 'field howitzer'.

Flak Flugabwehrkanonen. The German word for anti-aircraft guns.

Glacis The sloping armour on the front of a tank.

HE High Explosive.

HMC Howitzer Motor Carriage. The US designation for a howitzer on a tracked or half-tracked chassis.

Idler wheel The last wheel on a set of tracks. Not driven, but used to adjust track tension.

Mantlet Thick armoured piece covering the hole in the turret through which a tank's gun projects.

MG Machine gun.

Muzzle brake Device attached to the gun muzzle to reduce recoil by venting gases.

PaK Panzerabwehrkanone. German for anti-tank gun.

Panzerkampfwagen German for 'Armoured Fighting Vehicle', usually abbreviated to PzKpfw.

Panzerjäger German for 'tank hunter'.

Road wheel Wheel which is in contact with the part of the track that is on the ground.

Running gear The transmission, suspension, wheels and tracks of a tank.

Saukopfblende German meaning 'sow's head screen'. The very heavy gun mantlet used on some German tanks, such as the Hetzer.

Schürzen German for 'skirts' or 'aprons'. Thin steel screens used as spaced armour defence against light anti-tank weapons and explosive charges.

SdKfz Sonderkraftfahrzeug. German word for special purpose motor vehicle. Applied to almost all German vehicles except battle tanks.

SPG Self-propelled gun.

SPH Self-propelled howitzer.

Sprocket Wheel with teeth that transmits engine power to track. Also called Drive Wheel.

StuG Abreviation for Sturmgeschutze, meaning 'assault gun'.

SU Samokhodnya Ustanovka. Russian for self-propelled.

Support roller Small wheel that supports the upper part of the track between sprocket and idler.

Tank A tracked, well-armed and armoured fighting vehicle. In World War II and subsequently the name has come to mean only those such vehicles with fully rotating turrets and primarily designed to fight other tanks.

Tank Destroyer A US term for a lightly armoured but heavily armed tracked vehicle designed to ambush enemy AFVs.

Vertical Volute Spring Type of (US) suspension in which the road wheels are mounted on a bogie in pairs on arms, pivoting against a vertically mounted volute spring. Late war US tanks used a horizontal spring or HVSS suspension.

INDEX

Numbers in *italics* indicate illustrations.

A27M Cruiser Mk VIII, Cromwell V *212-13*, 214-17
Achtrad (8-rad) SdKfz 232 *54-5*, 56-7
AEC Mk III Armoured Car *228-9*, 230-1
air-portable tanks
　Kyrliati (KT) 275
　L3-35/Lf *118-19*, 120-1, 128
　M22 Locust *160-1*, 162-3
amphibious tanks
　T-40 274-5
　Valentine III 190-1
amphibious tractors (AMTRACs) 172, 174-5, 176, 178-9
anti-aircrafts tanks
　Leichte Flakpanzer 38(t) *98-9*, 100-1
　Ostwind, Flakpanzer IV 107, 109

Wirbelwind, Flakpanzer IV *106-7*, 108-9
Ardennes offensive 53, 97, 117, 170
armoured cars
　British 11, *228-9*, 230-1, *232-3*, 234-5
　German *54-5*, 56-7, *62-3*, 64-5
assault guns *see also* howitzers
　Churchill AVRE *204-5*, 206-7
　Sturmgeschütz III Ausf G *70-1*, 72-3, 92
　Sturmmörser Tiger *110-11*, 112-13
　SU-76 *292-3*, 294-5
　SU-152 *296-7*, 298-9

B1 bis *300-1*, 302-3, *308*
battles
　Ardennes 53, 97, 117, 170
　El Alamein 183, 187, 199, 222
　Gazala 153
　Kursk 39, 81, 84, 89, 296

Bergepanther V 38
BM-13 Katyusha 273, *288-9*, 290-1
British Universal (Bren) carrier 68
Brummbär, Sturmpanzer IV *86-7*, 88-9
BT-7 *252-3*, 254-5

C-54 Skymaster 163
C-82 Packet 163
Cadillac 166-7
Carden-Lloyd tankette 120
Carro Armato
　L6/40 *126-7*, 128-9
　M11/39 *122-3*, 124-5, 132, 188
　M13/40 125, 132-3
　M14/41 133
　M15/42 *130-1*, 132-3, 135, 137
Chaffee M24 *164-5*, 166-7
Char B1 bis 13, *300-1*, 302-3, *308*
Char B-ter *301*

Chi-Ha, Type 97 *142-3*, 144-5
Chi-Ni, Type 97 144
Christie suspension 11-12, *192*, *212*, 253, 254, *264*, *268*
Churchill
  AVRE *204-5*, 206-7
  Mk IV 11, *200-1*, 202-3, 207
  Mk VII Crocodile *208-9*, 210-11
Churchill, Winston 159
Crocodile, Churchill Mk VII *208-9*, 210-11
Cromwell
  Mk V *212-13*, 214-17
  Mk VI *217*, *218-19*
Cruiser
  Mk III 194
  Mk IVA 46, *192-3*, 194-5
  Mk VI, Crusader I 11, 192, *196-7*, 198-9
  Mk VIII, Cromwell V 11, *212-13*, 214-17
  Mk VIII, Cromwell VI 217, *218-19*

Crusader I, Mk VI Cruiser 192, *196-7*, 198-9
CV 33 light tanks *118-19*, 120-1, 124, 125, 128
CV L35 tankette *118-19*, 121
Czechoslovakia 7
  Jagdpanzer 38(t) Hetzer *102-3*, 104-5
  Panzer 38(t) *30-1*, 32-3, 105
  SdKfz 140 Leichte Flakpanzer 38(t) *98-9*, 100-1

DA 75/18 Semovente *134-5*, 136-7
Dieppe raid 201, 203, 206
Duplex Drive 190-1

Eastern Front 7, *36*, *37*, *45*, *46*, 65 see also Soviet Union
Kursk salient offensive 39, 81, 84, 89, 296, 299
El Alamein, Battle 183, 187, 199, 222

Elefant, Panzerjäger Tiger (P) *78-9*, 80-1

Ferdinand see Elefant
Fiat-Ansaldo 120, 128
Finland, Russian invasion 243, 247, 255, 259, 262
Firefly, M4A4 Sherman VC 11, 216, *220-1*, 222-3
flail tanks
  M4A4 Sherman V Crab II *224-5*, 226-7
  Matilda II 187
Flakpanzer IV
  Ostwind 107, 109
  Wirbelwind 101, *106-7*, 108-9
flamethrower tanks
  Churchill Mk VII Crocodile *208-9*, 210-11
  L3-35/Lf *118-19*, 120-1
  M4 Medium *157*
  Matilda II 187
  Valentine I 189

Food Machinery Company 175
France, Battle of 13, 307

gliders, Hamilcar 163
Grant Mk 1 *see* M3 Medium
Guderian, General Heinz
    39, 105

H-35 Hotchkiss *304-5*, 306-7
H-39 Hotchkiss *306*, 307
Ha-Go *see* Kyugo
half-tracked vehicles, SdKfz
    251 *58-9*, 60-1
Hamilcar gliders 163
Hanomag 60, 61
Henschel 44-5, 50, 53, 78
Hetzer, Jagdpanzer 38(t) *102-3*,
    104-5
Hitler, Adolf 24-5, 44, 52, 69, 81,
    88, 101
Hobart, General Percy 210
Honey *see* M3A1
Hotchkiss
    H-35 *304-5*, 306-7
    H-39 *306*, 307

howitzers *see also* assault guns
    Leichte Feldhaubitze 18/2
        14, *82-3*, 84-5
    M7B1 Priest Howitzer Motor
        Carriage *180-1*, 182-3
    M8 howitzer 176, 177, 178
    SdKfz 135/1 Lorraine
        Schlepper *66-7*, 68-9
    Sturmpanzer IV Brummbär
        86-7, 88-9
    Wespe *82-3*, 84-5
Hummel self-propelled gun
    85

Infantry Tank
    Mk II, Matilda II
        11, 125, *184-5*, 186-7
    Mk III, Valentine I 10, 13,
        125, *188-9*, 190-1, 238
    Mk IV, Churchill IV
        11, *200-1*, 202-3
IS-1 (Iosef Stalin 1)
    281, 283, 284, 286
IS-2 (Iosef Stalin 2)
    284-5, 286-7, 299

IS-3 (Iosef Stalin 3)
    13, 284, 287, 296
ISU-152 12, 296, 297, 299

Jagdpanther, SdKfz
    173 *94-5*, 96-7
Jagdpanzer
    see also tank destroyers
    IV/70 *90-1*, 92-3
    VI Jagdtiger
        52, *114-15*, 116-17
    38(t) Hetzer *102-3*, 104-5
    SdKfz 173 Jagdpanther
        94-5, 96-7
Jagdtiger, Jagdpanzer VI
    52, *114-15*, 116-17

Katyusha 273, *288-9*, 290-1
Kharkov Locomotive Factory
    266
King Tiger *50-1*, 52-3, 114,
    116
Korean War 10, 168, 295
Kursk salient offensive
    7, 39, 81, 84, 89, 296, 299

KV-1 12, 72, 296, 298
KV-1A 256-7, 258-9, 260, 261, 262, 281, 282
KV-2 260-1, 262-3
KV-7 298
KV-85 12, 280-1, 282-3
KW II(r), Sturmpanzer 263
Kyrliati gliding tank (KT) 275
Kyugo, Type 95 138-9, 140-1, 145

L3-35/Lf 118-19, 120-1, 128
L6/40 Carro Armato 126-7, 128-9
Lee see M3 Medium
Leichte Feldhaubitze 18/2 14, 82-3, 84-5
Leichte Flakpanzer 38(t), SdKfz 140 98-9, 100-1
Leningrad 45, 47
Locust M22 160-1, 162-3
Lorraine Schlepper, SdKfz 135/1 66-7, 68-9
LVT-1 174, 175
LVT-2 174, 175

LVT-4 Water Buffalo 172-3, 174-5, 178
LVT(A)-4 176-7, 178-9
LVT(A)-5 177, 179

M3 Medium 9, 124-5, 150-1, 152-3, 182, 236, 238
M3A1 Stuart III 9, 146-7, 148-9, 178, 179
M4 Medium 10, 141, 150, 161, 170, 180, 183
M4A2 Sherman III 9, 154-5, 156-9
M4A4 Sherman V Crab II 224-5, 226-7
M4A4 Sherman VC Firefly 11, 216, 220-1, 222-3
M5 Light Tank 9, 166-7
M7B1 Priest Howitzer Motor Carriage 180-1, 182-3
M8 howitzer 176, 177, 178
M11/39 Carro Armato 122-3, 124-5, 132, 188
M13/40 Carro Armato 125, 132-3

M14/41 Carro Armato 133
M15/42 Carro Armato 130-1, 132-3, 135, 137
M19 light tank 167
M22 Locust 160-1, 162-3
M24 Chaffee 164-5, 166-7
M26 Pershing 10, 168-9, 170-1
M37 Howitzer Motor Carriage (HMC) 167
M42 Semovente 136-7
Malta 263
Matilda II 11, 125, 184-5, 186-7
Maus 53, 114
Mitsubishi 145
Mk III Cruiser 194
Mk IVA Cruiser 46, 192-3, 194-5
Mk VI Cruiser, Crusader I 192, 196-7, 198-9

Nashorn, Panzerjäger IV 74-5, 76-7
Normandy, Allied landings 92, 121, 216-17, 311

Churchill 207, 208, 210-11
Panzer V Panther 38
Panzer VI Tiger I *44*, 45
Sherman V Crab II 224, 227
North African campaign 19, 24, 65, 188, 195, 230-1
Matilda II 184, 186, 187
Mk VI Cruiser, Crusader I 196, 199

Ostwind, Flakpanzer IV 107, 109

Panther 7, 223, 267, 270, 287
Ausf D *34-5*, 36-9, 50, 51
Ausf G 37, 38-9, *40-1*, 50, 51, 94, 96
Bergepanther V 38
Panzer I 6, 16
Panzer II 6, 82, 84, 129
Ausf F *14-15*, 16-17
Panzer III 7, 11, 17, 70, 72, 84, 217, 265, 293

Ausf H 17, *18-19*, 20-1
Ausf J (Special) *22-3*, 24-5
Panzer IV 7, 76, 217, 265
anti-aircraft tanks 101, 106, 107, 108
assault guns 84, 85, 86, 88
Ausf F1 *26-7*, 28-9
Jagdpanzer IV/70 90, 92
Panzer V Panther 7, 223, 267, 270, 287
Ausf D *34-5*, 36-9, 50, 51
Ausf G 37, 38-9, *40-1*, 50, 51
Bergepanther V 38
Panzer VI Tiger I *6*, 7, 110, 112, 223, 283, 287
Ausf E *42-3*, 44-7
Ausf H *48-9*, 51, 52
Panzer VI Tiger II *50-1*, 52-3, 114, 116
Panzer 38(t) *30-1*, 32-3, 105
see also Jagdpanzer 38(t); SdKfz 140

Panzerjäger
see also tank destroyers
IV Nashorn *74-5*, 76-7
SdKfz Jagdpanther 173 *94-5*, 96-7
Tiger (P) Elefant *78-9*, 80-1
Pershing M26 *168-9*, 170-1
personnel carriers
Ram Kangaroo 13, *236-7*, 238-9
SdKfz 251 *58-9*, 60-1
Poland, German invasion 16, 17, 20, 32, 57
Porsche *44-5*, 51, 78, 79, 80
Praga tank factory 104
Priest Howitzer Motor Carriage M7B1 *180-1*, 182-3
Puma, SdKfz 234/2 *62-3*, 64-5

Ram Kangaroo *236-7*, 238-9
Renault 303
R.35 *304*, 306
rocket weapons

BM-13 Katyusha
273, *288-9*, 290-1
Sturmmörser Tiger
110-11, 112-13
Roosevelt, President Franklin
159
Russo-Finnish War
243, 247, 255, 259, 262

S-35 SOMUA
306, *308-9*, 310-11
S-40 SOMUA 311
SdKfz
135/1 Lorraine Schlepper
66-7, 68-9
138/2 Hetzer *102-3*,
104-5
140 Leichte Flakpanzer
38(t) *98-9*, 100-1
173 Jagdpanther *94-5*, 96-7
231 (8-rad) 54
232 (8-rad) *54-5*, 56-7
234/2 Puma *62-3*, 64-5
250 39
251 *58-9*, 60-1

self-propelled guns *see* assault
guns; howitzers; tank
destroyers
Semovente
DA 75/18 *134-5*, 136-7
M42 136-7
Sherman *see* M4 Medium
Six Ton Tank, Vickers
240, 241, 242
Skoda tank factory 104
SOMUA
S-35 306, *308-9*, 310-11
S-40 311
Soviet Union, German invasion
of 244, 251, 255, 259, 266
see also Eastern Front
BM-13 Katyusha 290, 291
Panzer III 19, 20, 21
Panzer IV 28, 29
Panzer V Panther 36, 37
T-26A 240, 243
Spanish Civil War 247, 254-5
Staghound I, T17E1
232-3, 234-5
Stalin tank series 12

IS-1 281, 283, 284, 286
IS-2 *284-5*, 286-7, 299
IS-3 13, 284, 287, 296
Stalingrad 290
Stuart III M3A1
9, *146-7*, 148-9, 178, 179
Studebaker 6x6 trucks
288-9, 290
Sturmgeschutz
III Ausf G *70-1*, 72-3, 92
IV 93
Sturmmörser Tiger
7, *110-11*, 112-13
Sturmpanzer
IV Brummbär *86-7*, 88-9
KW II(r) 263
Sturmtiger 7, *110-11*, 112-13
SU-76 *292-3*, 294-5
SU-152 *296-7*, 298-9

T17E1 Staghound I
232-3, 234-5
T-26A *240-1*, 242-3
T26E3 170, *171*
T-28 *244-5*, 246-7

T-32 266
T-34 8-9, 22, 29, 252, 257, 294
    German response 7, 36, 72
    T-34/76A *264-5*, 266-7,
        270
    T-34/85 12, *268-9*, 270-1,
        281
T-35B *248-9*, 250-1, 256
T-40 272, 274-5
T-60 *272-3*, 274-5, 278, 279
T-70 *276-7*, 278-9, 292, 294
tank destroyers
    90-1, 92-3, *94-5*, 96-7
    Jagdpanzer 38(t) Hetzer
        102-3, 104-5
    Jagdpanzer IV/70 *90-1*,
        92-3
    Jagdpanzer VI Jagdtiger
        52, *114-15*, 116-17
    Panzerjäger IV Nashorn
        74-5, 76-7
    SdKfz 173 Jagdpanther
        94-5, 96-7
    Semovente DA 75/18
        134-5, 136-7

SU-76 *292-3*, 294-5
SU-152 *296-7*, 298-9
Tiger (P) Elefant *78-9*,
    80-1
Tetrach light tank 163
Tiger I *6*, 7, 110, 112, 223,
    283, 287
    Ausf E *42-3*, 44-7
    Ausf H *48-9*, 51, 52
    Jagdtiger 52, *114-15*,
        116-17
    Sturmmörser 7, *110-11*,
        112-13
Tiger II *50-1*, 52-3, 114, 116
Tracteur Blindé 37L 68
Treaty of Versailles 16, 56
Type 94 tankette 141
Type 95 Kyugo
    138-9, 140-1, 145
Type 97 Chi-Ha *142-3*, 144-5
Type 97 Chi-Ni 144

Valentine I 10, 13, 125, *188-9*,
    190-1, 238
Versailles, Treaty of 16, 56

Vickers Six Ton Tank
    240, 241, 242
Vomag 92-3
Voroshilov, Marshal Klementy
    259, 262

Water Buffalo LVT-4
    172-3, 174-5, 178
Wespe, Leichte Feldhaubitze
    18/2 14, *82-3*, 84-5
Western Europe, German
    invasion 13, 17, 32-3, 61,
    304, 307
Wirbelwind, Flakpanzer IV
    101, *106-7*, 108-9

Zimmerit anti-magnetic mine
    paste 40, 48, 70, 78